Water is a mirror reflecting our mind

Messages from Water

Messages from water
are telling us to
look inside ourselves

Messages from
water are telling
to look
inside ourselves

Messages from water
are telling us to
look inside ourselves

Masaru Emoto (Doctor of alternative medicine) / **I.H.M. General Research Institute**

HADO Publishing

CONTENTS

Introduction

Masaru Emoto, Water and HADO, which signifies the world of subtle energy related to consciousness, synonymous with "Chi" in Japanese

My first encounter with the study of water was when I became acquainted with Dr. Lee H. Lorenzen. Dr. Lorenzen was at that time 34 while I was 41. Dr. Lorenzen studied biochemistry at the University of California in Berkeley and later became a water researcher, developing "micro-cluster water" (or Magnetic Resonance Water).

Since the encounter with Dr. Lorenzen, I had become attracted to the study of water and wanted to know more about the properties of water. I wondered if there were any machines that could measure and see water. It was at this time that through Dr. Lorenzen, I learned about a machine that could measure HADO, called an MRA, Magnetic Resonance Analyzer. It was after this discovery that my research started to advance with increasing speed.

The MRA was used in the USA at that time for homeopathy (a popular alternative therapy in Germany). The minute that I saw this machine, an idea flashed through my mind that it could be used in the study of "micro-cluster water" (Magnetic Resonance Water), so I brought it back to Japan as an instrument that could hopefully contribute to my research.

As a result, "HADO water" which transcribes HADO information by MRAs in micro-cluster water, that Dr. Lorenzen produced at my request, demonstrated that the physical condition of people can be improved by water. I have introduced the use of MRA and HADO in my literary works as listed below. Please refer to these articles for specific details.

"The Prelude to the HADO Age" Sun Road Publishing Co., Ltd.
"Human Science of HADO" Business Publishing Co., Ltd.
"Truth of 'HADO' Theory" PHP Institute Inc.
"The Study of Water and Life from the Viewpoint of 'HADO' Science" PHP Institute, Inc.
"Food Science of HADO" Co-author, Akiko Sugahara Takanawa Publishing Co., Ltd.
"Happiness in Hard Times" Co-author, Ravi Batra PHP Institute, Inc.
"Saving Our World. The 'HADO' Theory Revolution" PHP Institute, Inc.
"HADO Theory Gives New Meaning to Human Happiness" PHP Institute, Inc.
"HADO: Tuning into a New Reality" PHP Institute, Inc.
"What is HADO?" PHP Institute, Inc.

"Awakening Latent Memory - In Search of a New Self" PHP Institute, Inc.
As I began doing more research on water, I became interested in taking pictures of various frozen water crystals. Through these pictures and by seeing these faces of water, I have gained a great amount of experience. These pictures were so wonderful that I just had to show them, so I decided to edit them into this picture book, "Messages from Water".

Water, Humans and Earth

A human being appears on this earth physically for the first time when an ovum of the mother and sperm of the father meet each other and become a fertilized egg. At this time water accounts for about 95% of the fertilized egg, in other words, it is almost all water. The amount of water in a matured human body is 70%. No wonder it is said that the human body is made of water.

People live their lives surrounded by various kinds of water everyday until the day they die. The earth is called the "Water Planet" and about 70% of its surface is covered with water. Isn't this somewhat similar to the human body? Most of the planet's water, such as rainwater, underground water, lakes, marshes and rivers, is in the sea. Some water floats in the air in the form of clouds or mist. Firn in high mountains and ice in Antarctic are also originally water.

As I went on with my research of water, I became unsure whether the precious water that I was working with was clean water or unclean water, and subsequently what it means to the human body. No one except for the people at a water research institution or water research professionals really knows the definite answer. Water, whatever its makeup, always appears the same to our eyes.
What is the difference in the information that each type of water holds? Is there any possible way of seeing that?
While I was thinking about this, I came across a book titled "The day that lightning chased the housewife" (edited by Julia Leigh and David Savold, Shobun-sha Publisher). This book contains about 50 questions. Among these, there was a question that asked "Are there any snow crystals of the same shape?" The answer was that snow has been falling on earth for a few million years, and each crystal has a different shape.

I had always wondered if there were methods of expressing the difference of water nature. And that was when it hit me: "This is it!" That was what led me to make these "pictures of frozen crystals of water" (hereafter referred to as crystals). With this method, all I had to do was to take pictures of the crystals made by freezing water.

If I freeze water and take a picture of the crystals that are formed, I could obtain information about the water. That was the whole idea behind the experiment that I was about to start.

I enlarged my pictures of crystals into slides and brought them to my lectures. Since then, I started to get requests for copies of them because of their beauty and mysteriousness. The loveliness as well as ugliness of the crystal pictures attracted people. It was from these events and my earnest desire to share the joy and mysteriousness of crystals that I decided to publish this book.

Masaru Emoto, Chairman of International HADO Membership

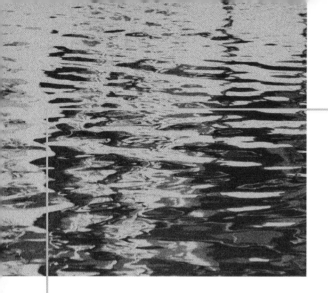

CHAPTER 1

The Story of Water in Daily Life

Water and Environmental Problems

We cannot think about the quantity of water that circulates this earth without thinking about environmental problems. To solve environmental problems we need to prevent water pollution, resulting in higher purification levels of water. Water circulates in this world limitlessly and absorbs and dissolves all contaminants. Water is the source of life. If water is contaminated, all creatures would be denied of their existence.

Considering these environmental situations, I continued to seek a way to clearly evaluate water.

Can the Water on Earth Survive?

The tap water that we use unconsciously everyday, is one type of water that has many appearances.

Most tap water is directly from rivers. River water is collected in a treatment plant to undergo sterilization and disinfection by chlorine. The water is then transported to each home through water pipes.

It has become common practice for home users in cities to attach a water purifier to the water faucet. Water in most cities is contaminated. How bad is the contamination and is it because the original river water is contaminated? Did it get contaminated on the way to the faucets at home?

How contaminated is natural spring water?

To go further back, how contaminated is the rain that falls from the sky contaminated? Does rainwater get contaminated with impurities in the air although it is to be distilled on earth?

Even scientific experiments and analyses of impurities and contaminants contained in each water sample seem to be partially a numeric magic.

Water is essential to our life, but when we think of it, it contains a lot of problems.

Where is tap water more contaminated, in Tokyo or Osaka?

How about cities in Hokkaido and Kyushu?

Is water in the rural areas really more pure?

While taking pictures of water crystals, we found that every kind of ice melts to water through the state shown in the picture. When water freezes, it becomes crystallized. At the moment right before it returns to its water form (with a rise in temperature, between -5°C and 0°C) it creates a shape that is identical to the Chinese character for water. Did people in the ancient times know this and make the Chinese character for "Water" based on this information?
To other letters except Chinese ones this reasoning may not be applicable.

Water Crystal is the Face of Water

Crystal is a solid substance with orderly configured atoms and molecules. In addition to appearing in snow and crystallized quartz, crystals are also seen in natural minerals such as diamonds, table salt, and chemical seasoning like MSG.

Because snow is formed under a variety of conditions, there are no crystals that have the same face (as is true for people's faces.)

This is due to the fact that for snow flakes to have the same crystal structure, the various types of water on earth have to have the same crystal structures to begin with.

I had a theory. When a water molecule crystallizes, pure water becomes pure crystal, but contaminated water may not crystallize as beautifully. Well, at least I thought so.

In 1994, I started my experiment.

I needed to get each sample of water frozen. Then before they melted I had to place these small fragile crystals on the microscope stage to be photographed at a super high speed.

First of all, I had to get a full set of equipment: the required quantity of water samples to freeze, Petri dishes of a material and volume that had to be considered, dry ice and a cooler. Photographing the crystals could only be possible after meeting various conditions: the exact freezer temperature, specific cooling time, exact refrigerator temperature, microscopic observation magnification, how to light the object, and the lens iris.

It took about 2 months before I was able to take a picture that I was satisfied with. During this period, I must have wasted hundreds or thousands of rolls of film.

However, it was a very impressive moment when I succeeded in taking my first picture of a water crystal. (Picture on page 15.)

After this initial photograph, my experiment gained momentum. I then made a refrigerated room in which a small freezer and a microscope set with a camera could fit. After organizing a "crystal photographing group" my colleagues and I took pictures one by one and stored the data.

The first successful crystal picture we took/micro-cluster water.

Discovery of a New Water Evaluation Method

Water changes rapidly and is unstable. We dropped one sample of water to be tested on 100 Petri dishes and placed them in a freezer for 2 hours. We took the crystals out and put them under the microscope to be photographed at magnifications of 200-500 times.

In order to obtain an example of an average crystal we had to photograph as many samples under as many conditions we could think of. It's only physically possible for most people to stay for about 30 minutes (at the longest) inside a refrigerator set at 5°C below zero while taking pictures.

It is impossible to obtain identical crystal pictures. In other words, it is impossible to perfectly reproduce the same crystal twice. However, crystals can show a certain distinctive tendency called a grid crystal or laminar crystal structure. Crystals can be identified by this structural tendency.

On page 78, there are pictures of crystals taken by freezing 100 samples at a time for 1 type of water. Although there are many examples of crystals in these samples such as beautiful crystals, hexagonal crystals, variable crystals, or no crystal, we can see that there is a certain tendency in all of the samples to form a grid crystal structure.

We learned many things from these pictures of crystals.

Thanks to the cooperation of several companies and volunteers, we were able to take pictures of spring water, rainwater, river water, lakes and marshes in Japan and all across the world.

We have photographed and stored about 10.000 pictures in 4 and a half years.

Most of the water from overseas shown in this picture collection was collected by Mr. Tetsuya Taguchi, the former President of Nichirei Ice Co., Ltd., who traveled all over the world and wrote "The Cultural History of Ice: Links between Man and Ice," published by the Reitou Shokuhin Journal.

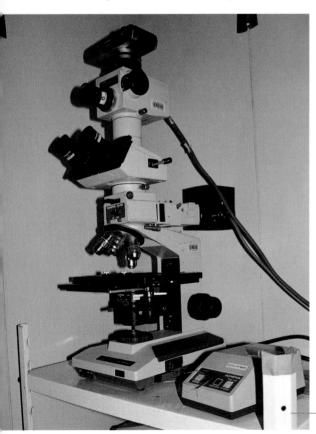

Camera

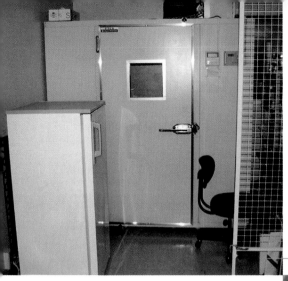

Freezer water to be tested is divided into 100 Petri dishes for freezing.

Placing a drop of water to be tested into a Petri dish using a pipette.

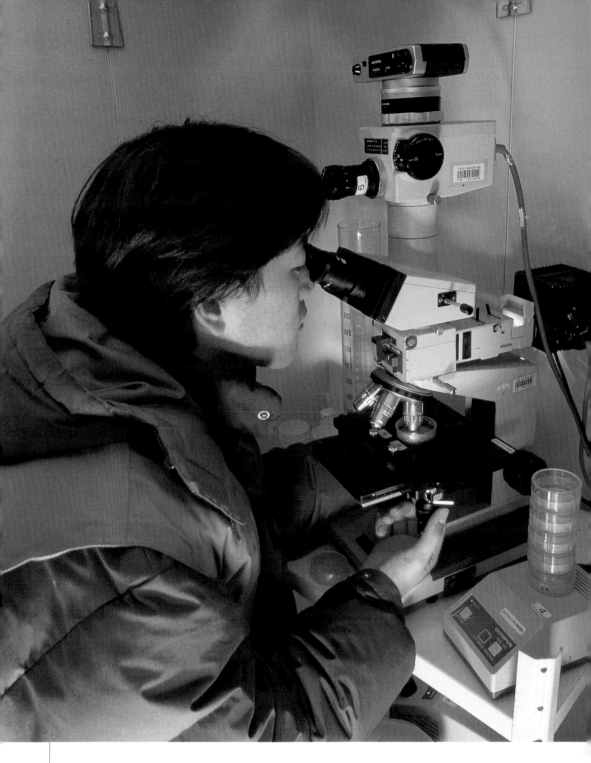

Photographing inside a
refrigeration room at -5°C.

When our staff actually looks at the crystal picture, it is most important that they notice that it has a completed "hexagonal crystal structure", as we saw in the first picture. From our experience, we know that the chipping away and/or the collapsing of crystal structures are not good signs. In other words, the judgment criteria is whether you can feel that it is beautiful or not by looking at it.

During the photographing, we observed the crystallization process a few thousand times. Then strangely, we came to feel and see the crystal trying to become "beautiful crystal figure" of water, and we saw that crystal pictures carry wonderful messages. We felt that the water was trying to say something to us. We came to understand that these crystal pictures show different "faces of water".

Water, basically, is trying hard, and bravely it shouts "Clear water! I want to be clear water!" We felt that such an outcry was expressed by the crystals of water.

Pictures of crystallized water may deviate slightly from the information given by modern scientific water analysis. Our water evaluation method comes at the analysis from a completely different angle.

In addition, as is often quoted, "The energy flow of people as well as water is not stable." The pictures of the water crystals express the condition of that sample of water only at that very moment of that very day.

Therefore, in order to raise this analysis to a scientific level, the crystals had to be observed on a daily basis at various locations and analyzed with the support of many people. This is perhaps the first attempt of this kind in the world. We hope you will enjoy this introduction to a unique way of approaching the study of water, called the "Faces of water".

Photographing the ice tip.

Tap Water,
in Japan

Picture of Tap Water Crystals

Regretfully, it is a known fact that chlorine, chlorinated tri-halomethane and other chemical substances that are the causes of environmental hormones are found in the tap water of Japan. When we drink the tap water in major cities, we actually smell a chlorine odor.

We all know that this is one of the reasons why the tap water in Japan is not good.

The water that comes from dams and rivers has disinfectants added to it to make it drinkable. And since it carries a sign saying, "Added disinfectants are not harmful to humans," we are supposed to believe that it is OK. Actually though, many people use water purifiers to remove the seemingly harmful substances that they instinctively know threaten their bodies.

The ratio of waterworks covering local and rural areas is nearly 100% in Japan. These days, only a small amount of people pump up underground water or well water to use it as drinking water.

There is a specific nationwide standard for tap water, and the law makes sure that the water that doesn't satisfy these standards cannot be supplied to the public.

I decided to take pictures of tap water samples in their crystal forms. Do tap water samples that meet the national standards have the same kind of crystals no matter where in Japan the samples are found?

Sapporo, Hokkaido Prefecture

Sapporo is a large city, but when comparing its suburban environment with the suburbs of Tokyo, nature is more intact. The source of the tap water in Sapporo comes from the Toyohira River. Although this river is not as badly polluted as some others, we could not obtain clear crystals from this tap water.
However, it seems that it is trying desperately to be clean.

Sendai City, Miyagi Prefecture

Sendai is famous as the "City of Forests" and it has beautiful water sources. But as for its tap water, it is the same as Sapporo's.

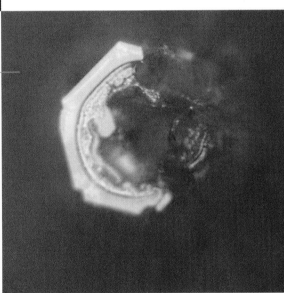

Kanazawa City, Ishikawa Prefecture

Kanazawa is the largest city in the Hokuriku district and it is a castle town.
The Asano River and the Sai River flow through the city, and Kenrokuen Park at the center of the city has one of the 3 famous gardens of Japan.
However, the water is…

Shinagawa-ku, Tokyo

This picture seems to indicate that the water in Tokyo is not as good as we had expected.
This picture of Tokyo's tap water shows no sign of crystallization. Is this the fate of water in a metropolitan environment?

Nagoya City, Aichi Prefecture

Unexpectedly, we were able to capture its figure just before crystallization, rarely seen in tap water in large cities. The water source is the Kiso River.
What is the factor that prevents a water crystal from forming a complete hexagon?

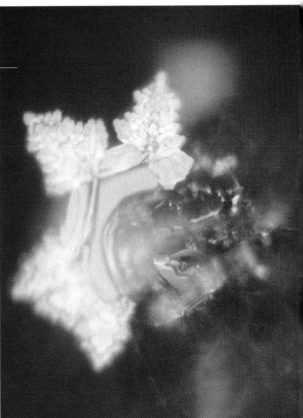

Kita-ku, Osaka City

Osaka used to be a "City of Water". But it has become a city famous for unpalatable water. The sample of water from Osaka seems to be trying to crystallize, though it is significantly distorted. We can see branches at the corners, which indicate that it is trying to become fully developed.

Katano City, Osaka Prefecture

Katano City lies in the northern part of Osaka and on the prefectural border between Nara and Kyoto.
We were able to obtain a clear crystal from the tap water in Katano, since 60% of it comes from an underground water source. Come to think of it, Sen-no-Rikyu, a tea master and a founder of the Sen school of tea ceremony, used water from Katano to make tea.

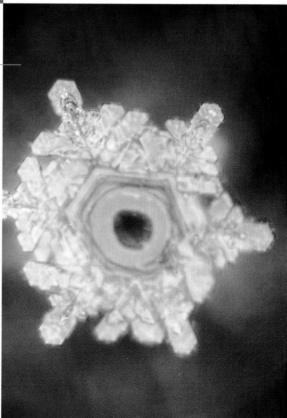

Hiroshima City, Hiroshima Prefecture

Hiroshima, a city of rivers and bridges.
Hiroshima, a city baptized by the atomic bomb.
Saijo is famous for its sake, and the water in
this city has been good since ancient times.
The crystal that is trying hard to develop into a
hexagon seems to be expressing the graceful
kindness and solidarity of its people.

Fukuoka City, Fukuoka Prefecture

The largest city in Kyushu, Fukuoka. Is it an
impossible task to try to obtain a clear crystal
from city tap water? About half of the crystals
that we photographed seemed to have been
eroded by something, but it still shows traces of
a crystal shape.

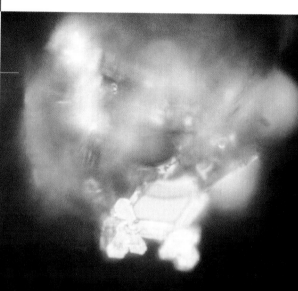

Naha City, Okinawa Prefecture

Okinawa is mainly a tourist and commercial
city. On the island, the cherry blossom season
starts about 1 to 2 months earlier than on the
mainland and its rainy season also starts earlier.
There are no large rivers so the water source
for its tap water comes from rainwater
reservoirs.
This water crystal seems to express the
people's warm feelings toward water and
the sea.

Tap Water,
Overseas

Each country has its own customs. Nothing is changed as much by the environment and the natural features of the land (including civilization and culture) as the water.

For this reason, the WHO (World Health Organization) created water guidelines in 1984. In these guidelines it is stated that "The standard for safety judgment of drinking water and criteria for treatment should be determined by each country giving consideration to its own domestic conditions (water circumstances, environmental level of the entire society, technical as well as economical power) and these guidelines are only provided as a basic material for that purpose." Therefore, the water purification method for tap water differs for each country. In our country, a treatment system using mainly chlorine has been provided by the ministerial ordinance of each prefecture. These pictures of tap water crystals from around the world were taken from only 6 large cities: London (UK), Paris (France), New York (USA), Vancouver (Canada), Buenos Aires (Argentina) and Manaus (Brazil). However, when compared with the pictures of Japanese water crystals, they were surprisingly clearer. It seems that the reason is the difference in the degree of contamination of the water sources in each country, as well as the difference in the water treatment systems.

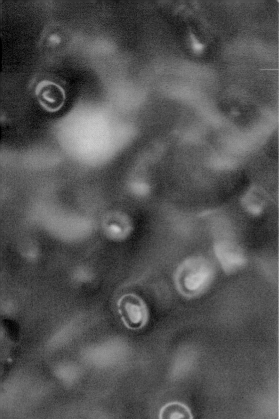

London, UK

Tap water from London, a foggy city.
We could only obtain crystals that were not
fully developed as they frequently were in the
case of Japan.

Paris, France

The tap water of Paris where the
Seine River flows.
The sample did not crystallize easily, but it was
not as bad as we had expected.

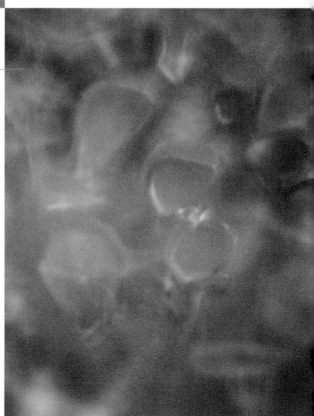

New York, USA

New York is located on the east coast of the North American continent and is said to be a cultural melting pot.

We can see that some of the top water crystals have better faces than those from Japanese spring water.

In New York, tap water is usually fluorinated or ozonized.

Vancouver, Canada

Vancouver is located on the west coast of the North American continent.
Seattle, Washington, in the USA is just a few miles south.
Because the weather is relatively warm and subsequently gives its population a comfortable living climate, many Japanese people live in Vancouver. The crystals of the water here retained a beautiful crystalline shape that is specific for tap water.

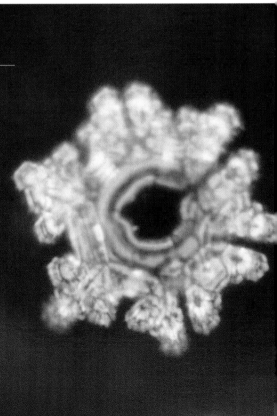

Buenos Aires, Argentina

The water here shows a beautiful crystal shape.
Pictures of these beautiful crystals remind us of how bad Japanese tap water is.
Beautiful crystals, however, are one thing, safe drinking water while traveling is another.

Manaus, Brazil

Very beautiful crystals.
The water crystallized beautifully. The people who live in countries where the tap water is drinkable are really very fortunate, but the disinfection criteria are not so exacting as those in Japan.

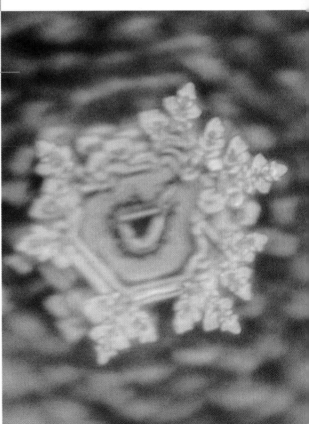

Water in the
Natural World

Water Flows Swiftly... is a Natural Figure of Water

We talk about "natural water", but what does the word "natural" really mean? In other words, the boundaries of the word natural are very vague. If we say that water "not influenced by humans" is natural water, then there may be no water left on earth that can be called natural.

Water existed on earth long before humans arrived. It has repeated its swift circulation cycle naturally.

We were only borrowing circulating "natural" water.

We were just borrowing it, but because it became so convenient, we started using too much water as our human culture developed. As a result, we started polluting water before we put it back in circulation. This polluted water is then "disinfected" with chlorine, which we call purification, thus creating "unnatural" water.

Purifying Power of Circulating Water

Water is originally natural and has the power to purify itself. For instance, when rainwater penetrates the ground, it is filtered through the soil and becomes part of an underground water source. Water also is filtered when it evaporates from rivers and lakes to become clouds in the sky. These are just some of its natural processes of purification.

Creatures that live between the river and the sea, such as corbicula, goby and striped mullet, eat their food that is carried from upstream. Therefore, it can be said that as a result of this natural purification, the water near the river mouth would show beautiful crystals as compared to the water found midstream.

Where Can You Find Natural Water?

Amidst the great circulation cycle of nature, purification is always happening on a large scale. However, today, due to the work of humans, a large amount of chemical substances have penetrated the soil through which rainwater filters. This means that underground water sources and spring water also are contaminated.

Not to mention the contamination that occurs when rivers take in waste water from sewage treatment facilities and plants, grey water, exhaust gas from automobiles, soot and smoke from plants, and smoke from incinerating daily industrial waste materials are also contamination sources just like many nuclear power plants that are being built.

Air is polluted under all kinds of conditions. Rainwater as "acid rain" is also subject to pollution by humans.

Lakes and marshes have been artificially reformed by damming, reclamation, covering, dissipating and were even moved.

It indeed requires effort to find "natural" water in the true sense of the word.

In this chapter, we will show a collection of pictures of the water crystals found in typical natural springs, rivers, lakes, marshes and finally in rainwater. Most of the samples are mainly gathered in Japan as "water not polluted by human hands."

Spring Water

The Natural Face of Spring Water

These photographs of spring water collected from all across Japan are very interesting. Photographing was thrilling especially when compared with the depression that we felt while taking the pictures of the tap water crystals.

Mountains cover about 80% of Japan. Because of this we have an abundance of natural mountains and forests not commonly seen in industrialized countries. We have plenty of rain and are blessed with pure water.

Since ancient times, this environment and our many natural springs have been closely related to the long and healthy life span of our rural people.

However, with rapid urban development and artificial development of mountains and forests, increased water supply accesses and drainage systems were built after World War II. Because of this, many sources of spring water became unusable due to contamination or simply to drying up.

But recently, the community was alerted to the dangers of tap water, and this (triggering a "mineral water" boom) has drawn attention to natural spring water again.

"Selected 100 waters of Japan" has been featured in magazines. To seek such water sources, some people travel hours to the identified locations. These are pictures of selected natural spring water crystals.

Now, what kind of faces do the natural spring water and ground water have and what message do they convey?

Water here comes from a limestone cave that holds an underground lake as deep as 120 meters in some places.

Although the crystal that is formed from this water is partially chipped, we feel a dynamic strength coming from its structure. The water from the underground lake seems to desperately try to preserve its uncontaminated nature even if eroded. We believe that we must make the earth beautiful again, before it is too late.

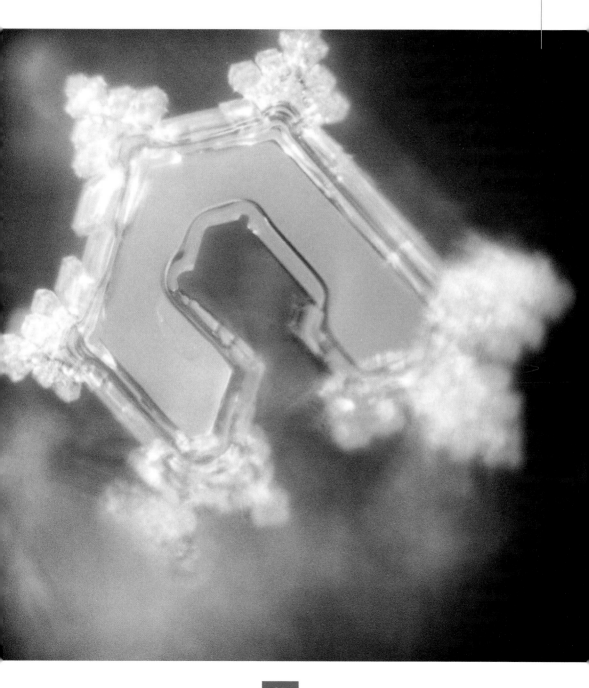

Sanbu-ichi Yusui Spring Water, Nagasaka-cho, Kita-Koma-gun, Yamanashi Prefecture

From a sample that was made up of Sanbu-ichi Yusui spring water we were able to obtain a beautiful crystal. It is made up of snow water, from Mr. Yatsugatake.

Based on a well-balanced hexagonal structure, 3 branches stretch out from each corner of the crystal. This gives the impression of people holding hands together around the spring water.

Clear Water of Kobo, Kanagawa Prefecture

Originating from Kobo Daishi, this spring is said to never dry up even during a severe draught. The products sold at the local tourist centers, including sake and soba, advertise that they are made using water from this spring.
Looking at the picture of the crystal we feel a strong power that seems to come from underground.
We want to hand down wonderful treasures to our future generations.

Kobo Spring Water, Fukuyama City, Hiroshima Prefecture

About 1,200 years ago, the great Buddhist teacher Kobo was traveling in the Chugoku region of Japan. Many people in the region were affected by a strange illness and to help them Kobo hammered away the base rock with his staff in order to get at the natural water flowing underneath. This water was named Kobo Spring Water.
The name "Kobo Spring Water" is found in various places throughout Japan, wherever natural hot waters sprang forth during Kobo's travels.
These are two very similar types of Kobo Spring Water. They are so similar that even our staff sometimes has trouble telling them apart.

Rumbling Water in Tenkawa Village, Yoshino-gun, Nara Prefecture

This name comes from the rumbling echoing sound that this spring makes. The spring lies in a limestone cave at the entrance of a mountain path in the Omine Mountains. The people of these mountains are famous for their worshipping practices and strict ascetic beliefs. The water that gushes from the mouth of this cave spring is called mystic water for this reason.

This town that sprawls in the highlands mountains 500 to 700 meters above sea level is famous as a sake brewing area: the water here is very good. It is as famous for sake as Nada in Hyogo Prefecture and Fushimi in Kyoto are.

The crystal that this spring water forms is firm through the center and branches magnificently. It then spreads out fully, leaving no empty space.

Ubuyama's Water, Kumamoto Prefecture

Ubuyama's water is a spring located at the northern end of Kumamoto Prefecture, which borders Oita Prefecture and lies at the foot of the Aso Mountain where cattle breeding is prosperous. It is also of the source of the Ono River, one of the "Selected 100 waters of Japan".
This beautiful crystal is just like a delicate flower blossom.

"St. Lourdes' Fountain" is said to be a fountain of miracles. The water has HADO from love and it reverses hatred into love. More than 4 million people from every corner of the world come to visit each year.

This crystal expresses the merits of the collective consciousness. A mysterious crystal that gives off the feeling of mystical glory.

Hogget Diamond Spring Water in Tasmania, Australia

The Tasmania region is located at the south-eastern end of Australia. The spring is located in a Paleozoic era rock formation where opal and diamond mining (for industrial use) once prospered.

It is no wonder that glittering crystals of diamonds were found.

This is once of the most popular tourist attractions for Japanese people. The climate is such that while the seacoast offers warmth enough for swimming, the mountain provide the temperatures needed for skiing. The underground water of the country where the number of sheep exceeds the number of people, is preserved and taken over by people who cherish tradition.

Rivers, Lakes and Marshes

Water that Supports Life

The rain that falls on the mountains and forests can become nutrition for trees or penetrate through the soil to form small streams underground. With enough water these streams become wide and strong, forming a river. These rivers then gradually accumulate enough energy and water to pass through steep mountains, carrying with it the nutritious mountain soil.

Depending on the terrain along the way, the water may form pools, ponds, lakes or marshes. By carrying water downstream, the river nurtures creatures as well as plants. When the river enters a plain it enriches the fields as it advances ahead by depositing the fertile soil that it carried from upstream.

Most of the food put on our tables everyday could not have grown without the blessings of the river water.

In Japan we have no large rivers but we do have an abundant number of small rivers, lakes, ponds and marshes. Even these small rivers have been important to our people's lives since ancient times and have contributed in supplying drinking water, as well as providing a means of transportation and field irrigation.

The flow of the rivers that are directly connected with our lives is very important to us.

How badly contaminated are the rivers that flow through cities?

What are the conditions in the local areas?

What is the appearance of the water crystals of the rivers that we describe as limpid streams?

What kinds of images does the water crystal of the lakes and marshes, the source of rivers show?

Horobetsu River, Hokkaido

This river flows from central Hokkaido south-
wardly, through the foothills of the Hidaka
Mountain range, on to the Horobetsu River
and eventually into the sea. These beautiful
crystals look just like flower petals.

I am impressed that there is a still river in Japan
that has such beautiful crystals.

The name originated from the look of the water's surface in the dotted marshes at the entrance of the Bandai Plateau. The surface of the water there can be seen changing into 5 colors ranging from red and blue to green.

This change in color is thought to be affected by the deposits from the marsh bottom combined with the effects of solar rays. A water crystal glitters beautifully during the spring snow melting season.

Upstream, Tokamachi-bashi

Shinano River, Niigata Prefecture

Pictures of the water crystals found upstream, midstream and downstream in the Shinano River as it flows across the Niigata prefecture and Nagano prefecture.

You can see by the crystals that the river is gradually contaminated as it flows into an urban area.

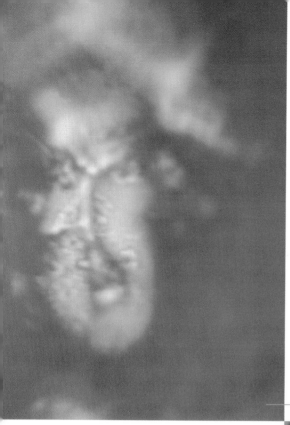

Midstream, Nagaoka City

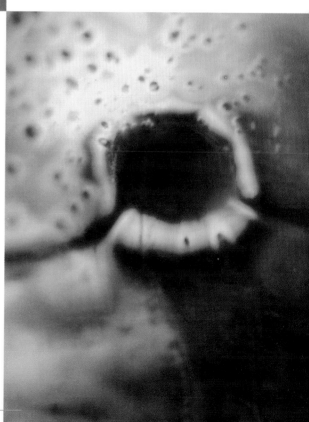

Downstream

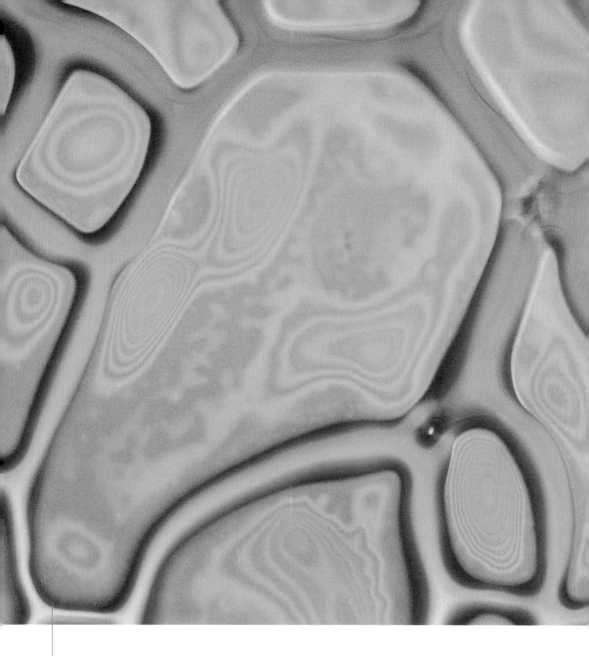

Sumida River, Tokyo

Cherry blossom trees bloom along the Sumida River, attracting many people.
The actual crystallized face of the river water that flows beneath the cherry blossom trees looks like this. Isn't it a little bit sad?

It is hard to say such a thing because it has actually become more beautiful now than it was 20 or 30 years ago.

There is a large city midstream the Fuji River, but that area also seems to be contaminated. But the water crystals found at the rivers mouth are clear because of the purifying affects of the fish and shells living in the vicinity.

This water crystal appears to have the intention of going back to the beautiful sea.

Upstream, Metori Yusui Spring Water

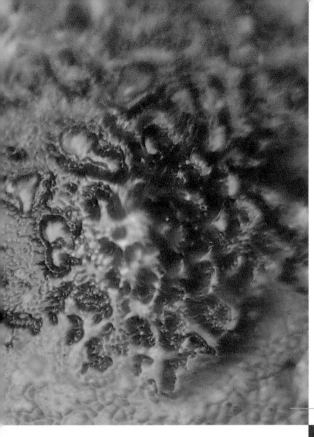

Midstream

Mouth of river

The Ado River flows north of Hira Mountain in Shiga Prefecture to the Biwako Lake.
The river passes through the town of Takashima which is the production center of Kyosen, Japanese traditional fan of folk crafts.

The beautiful crystal reflects the traditional work craft of Japan.
How will this crystal's form change once it pours into the Biwako Lake?

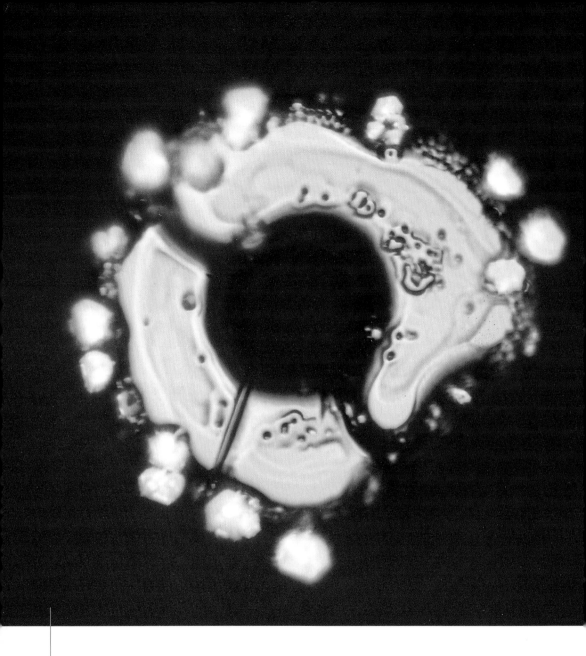

Biwako Lake (South Area of the Lake), Shiga Prefecture

The largest lake in the center of Japan and the water pool of the Kinki Region. Regretfully, the water of Biwako Lake seems to be like this. This crystal's structure supports the fact that the contamination of Biwako Lake is getting worse each year. This is the case, even though the Shiga Prefecture has for many years been making efforts through its campaign against the usage of synthetic detergents. This is a picture of the water crystal's lamentable figure.

The Yodo River pours into the Bay of Osaka as it flows southward, enriching the entire Kinki plain.

The river passes through most of the major cities in Kansai and flows as if it literally has been given as the role of a general cleaning in its path. It must be suffering from the load of contamination accumulated from its daily life and all of the people that it touches.

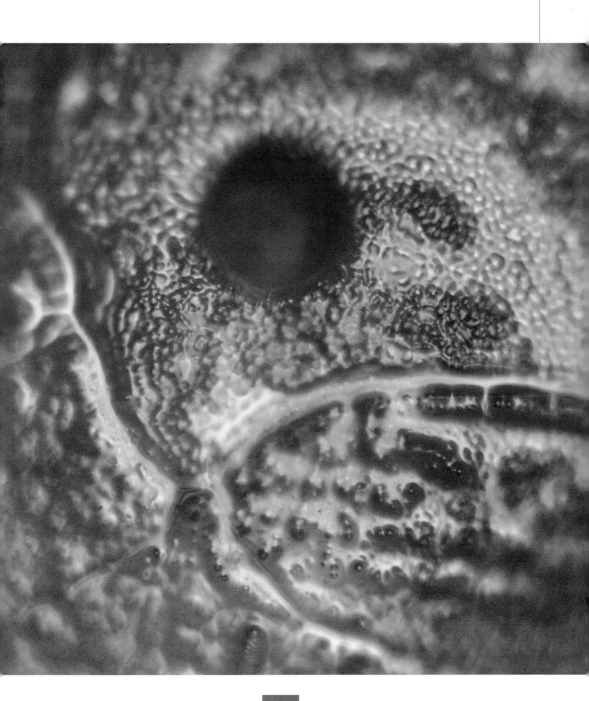

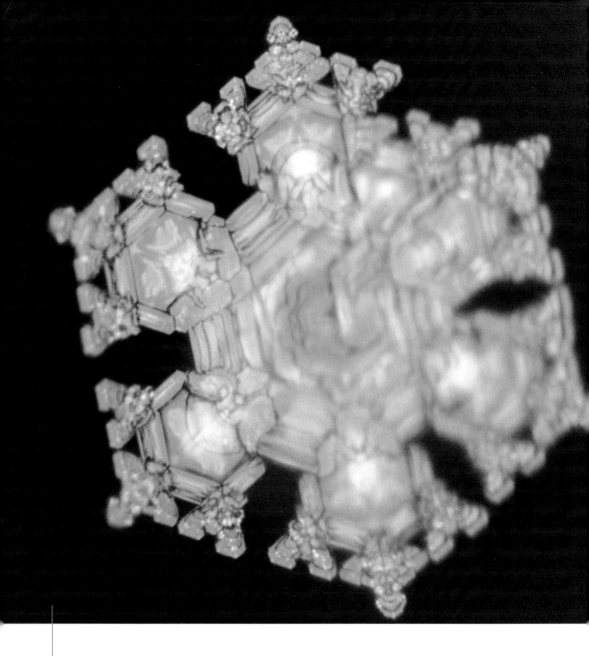

Shimanto River, Kochi Prefecture (Midstream)

The Shimanto River is referred to as the last clean stream in Japan. It creates a beautiful crystal which features in the branches.
At the outside of the basic hexagon structure, a hexagon branch is attached and from its edge another small branch stretches out.

This beautiful crystal was taken from the middle section of the river. Within its structure we can feel the spirit of citizens that lived along the river.

Glaciers

Ice on the earth can be divided into roughly two types: ice on land and ice on sea. A glacier is located on land, at places other than lakes, rivers, and frozen soil. A glacier forms from snow that has accumulated over a long period of time. An accumulation of snow at the middle of a mountainslope that looks like a river is called a glacier.

In the winter, snow accumulates rapidly into large piles that will become glaciers. Before the temperature becomes higher and starts to melt the snow, winter comes again. With the repetition of this cycle, normally, in more than a few years the glaciers turn to ice. For regions with little snow it takes more than 100 years for a glacier to form. Glaciers are labeled by where they occur geographically, such as, plateau glaciers, mountain glaciers, valley glaciers, suspension glaciers and mountain foot glaciers. Glaciers have a history. Glaciers have ice stratums in the same way that geological formations have stratums. I have this big dream of taking a sample of these stratums some day to survey these ancient water crystals.

The pictures of glacial water crystals shown here are of samples taken from the surface of the glaciers: they are considered to be affected by the present global environment.

This is a crystal of ice that one of the Antarctic expedition members brought back. It is estimated to be 370.000 years old. This crystal is very organized and is a perfect model of crystal formation. However, it is not as markedly beautiful as some other natural spring water crystals that we have seen. This means that today's natural water is not as contaminated as it was at one time in history. This is quite a relief.

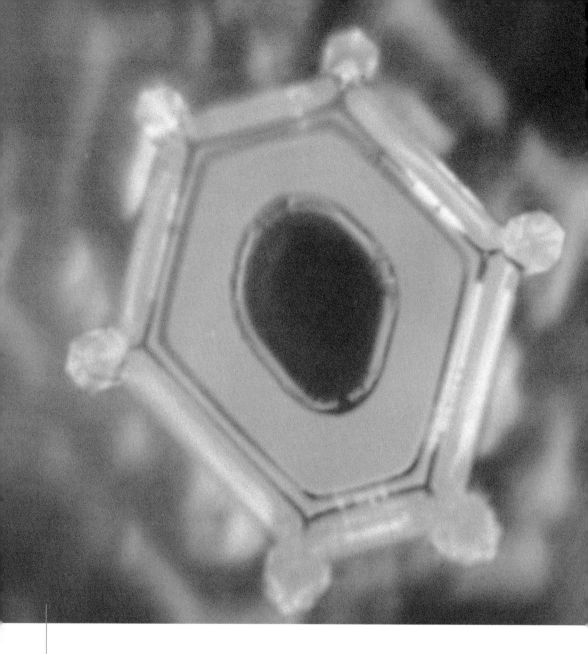

Colombian Glaciers, Canada

There are many glaciers in the Canadian Rocky
Mountains.
This crystal of ice is extracted from perputual

snow and maintains a firm hexagonal shape.
What kind of message is expressed by the large
void at the center of the crystal?

New Zealand is an island country located in the southwest Pacific Ocean, southeast of Australia.

It consists of North Island and South Island. In North Island's central area there is an active volcano that is still in good shape.

On South Island, there are mountains that exceed 3,000 meters. Among them is Mount Cook which is as high as Mount Fuji and has a glacier. This is the picture of a crystal taken from the melting water of that glacier.

Rainwater

Rain comes falling down from heaven.

All year round, the same amount of rain falls on the same land.

Because of this consistency, people can plan and grow crops, drink water, and pump water; and trees in the mountains get enough water.

The water of the earth becomes rain as it evaporates into the sky and then falls back onto the ground. It is cleansed by passing through this natural water purification process.

What we learn from this crystal's picture is that of course natural purification is much more effective than any mechanical water purifier, no matter how good.

Rain is the source of fresh water such as spring water, lakes, marshes and rivers.

We obtained this beautiful crystal from natural spring water.

The spring water that flows out onto the earth's surface passed through the natural filtering devices of soil and rocks when it fell as rain a few hundred years ago and penetrated into the ground.

The water then joins the spring water vein to flow out at a place that it feels is "the right place" and *when* it feels that it is "the right time".

What would the crystals look like from this rain which is the source of spring water?

We sampled rainwater and took a picture of the crystal.

Recently, there have been reports of damage due to environmental disruption. What is the water crystal difference between rain that falls on a densely populated urban area and rain that falls on a rural area?

Is there a difference between the rain that falls in the north or the south? Is there any difference between the rain that falls in different seasons at the same location?

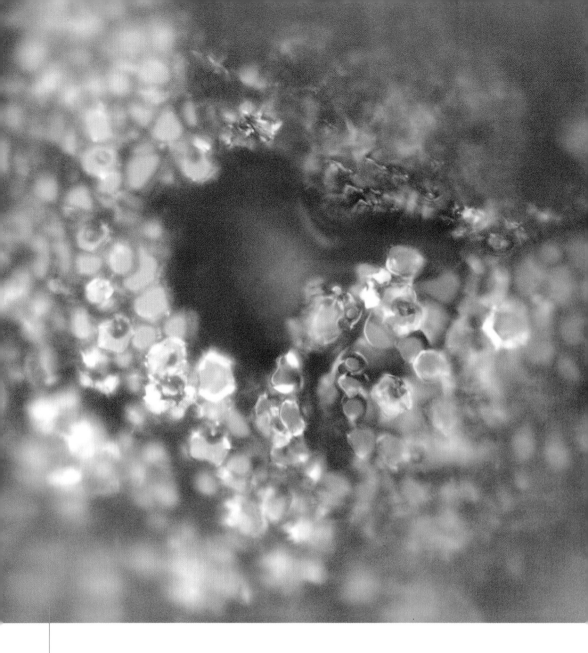

Biei-cho, Hokkaido

Located in the center of Hokkaido, Biei-cho was chosen as one of the locations for the movie "Kita-no-Kuni Kara, From the Northern Country."
The crystals from the rainwater that falls on this quiet rural region are saddening. Hokkaido seems to have suffered obvious damage caused by ozone layer depletion and acid rain.

Sendai City, Miyagi Prefecture

The rainwater from the Sendai area sometimes showed beautiful crystals and sometimes showed crystals with an unshapely form. There were also great fluctuations in the crystals depending on the season.

The cause is not clear but rainwater seems to be very delicate and might have been affected by the condition of atmosphere at that time.

Kanazawa City, Ishikawa Prefecture

From the rain that falls on the ancient city of Kanazawa, we obtained mysterious crystals. The crystal is not complete, but we can see a hexagonal crystal structure.

There aren't as many large industrial zones on the Japan Sea coast as there are on the Pacific Ocean coast, so it would follow that the air pollution level in this area is lower. We feel that for this reason we should be able to obtain a beautiful water crystal from the Japan Sea coast than from the Pacific Ocean coast.

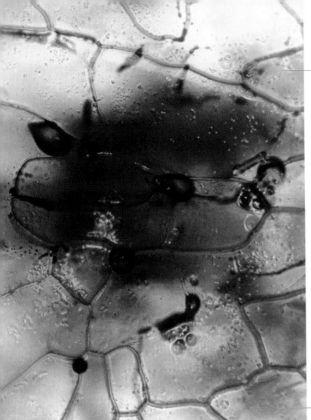

Tokorozawa City, Saitama Prefecture

When we first started taking pictures of the rainwater in Tokorozawa City (June, 1998), the crystal's structure was so miserable that we hesitated to publish it. However, as you can see in the picture on the right, the crystal has become clearer recently. We cannot help but believe that as the citizens of Tokorozawa became aware of their city's environmental problems, it has started to show some very beautiful crystals.
Stick to it, Tokorozawa!

June 1998

July 1998

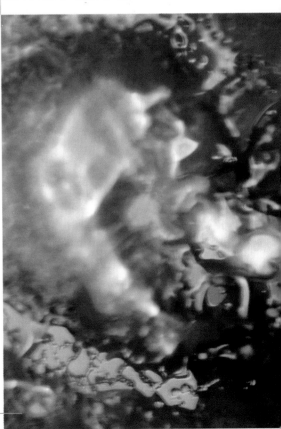

October 1998

December 1998

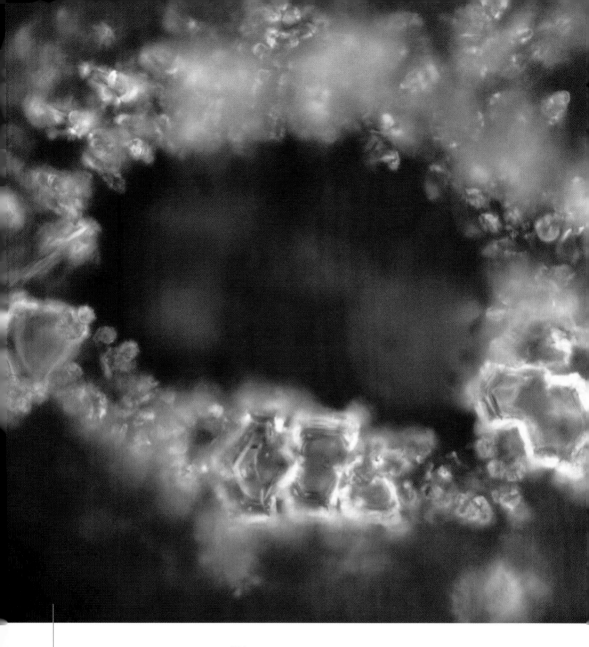

Tokorozawa
February 1999

We were able to get crystals from the rain that fell on the Asakusa-bashi at the center of Tokyo.

It was hard to find shapely and beautiful crystals from this water, but still, we can see the effects of the natural purifying power of rain water. This is especially evident when we compare them with the crystals found in tap water.

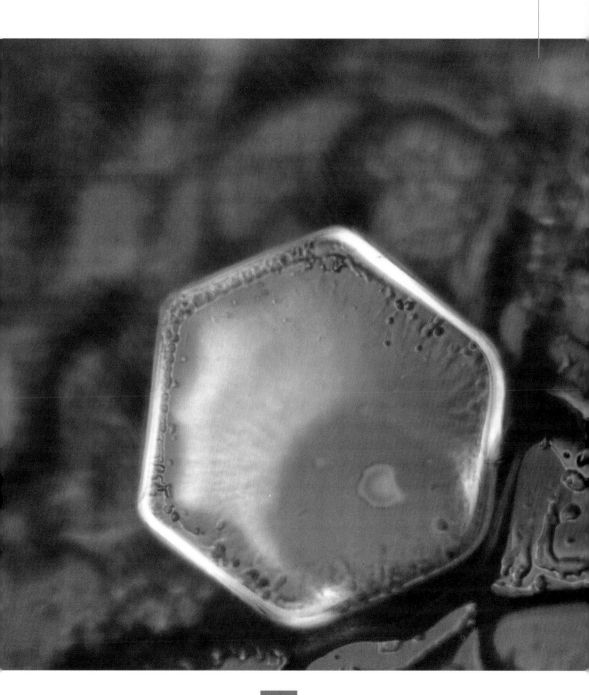

Fujisawa City, Kanagawa Prefecture

Fujisawa is a historic city near Enoshima and in a prestigious residential area. The city has beautiful scenery, is comfortable and easy to live in. However, because of acid rain, the rainwater crystal from this area melted away, leaving no trace of a hexagonal shape.

We could not see an organized shape in the crystal taken from the rainwater in Okazaki City where is adjacent to Nagoya City. At one point we could see crystals that were close to formulating, but the factors that impeded their formation seemed to be stronger.

While looking at these crystals we felt a sense of chaos in the images. It is as if the water itself is irritated.

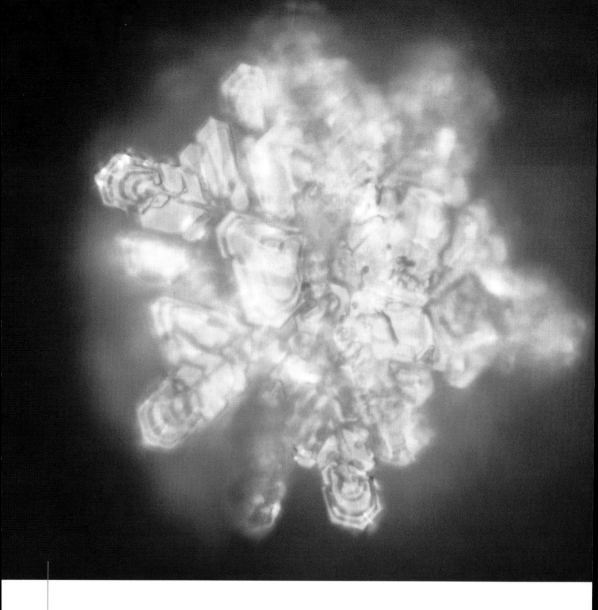

Nishi-ku, Osaka City

From the rainwater that was sampled from the office quarters of Osaka City we find the most beautiful picture of a crystal.

There is a distortion in the crystal and it has not become fully developed but we can see its will to become crystallized.

Fukuyama City is located on the coast of the Seto Inland Sea. It was re-developed after World War II because it was destroyed by bombing. In the crystal we can identify remnants of a hexagonal structure, but most of the crystal structure is either distorted or cracked. From these pictures however, we can feel that it is "trying hard" to develop and we want to support its efforts.

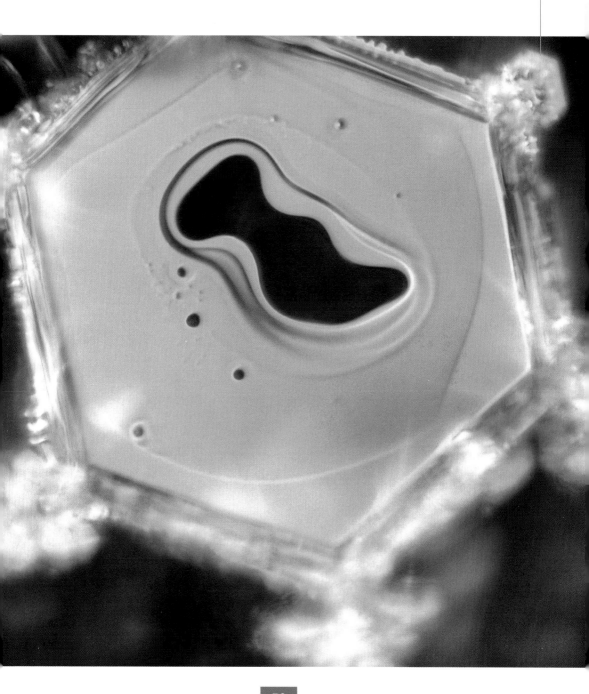

Hakata-ku, Fukuoka City

A crystal taken from a sample of the rain in Hakata, the largest city in Kyushu. Alas, this crystal could not evade the damage caused by acid rain.

The crystal shape is slightly distorted but seems to be a hexagon, and some of the clearer crystals have split in two. What is the water crystal trying to tell its city's citizens?

Kagoshima City, Kagoshima Prefecture

In this picture, we obtained the shape of a mystical figure imbedded in a clear crystal with branches stretching out from the hexagonal structure. As compared with the crystals from other cities, there is hope in this one.

We could not help but wonder what affect the volcanic ashes of Sakurajima have on the surrounding rainwater?

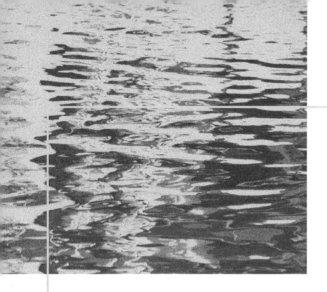

CHAPTER 2

A Story of Ever-Changing Water

Water Listens to Sound?

Recently, we see advertisements such as "Our piroshki is now a 'musical food'. We tried to enhance its naturally mellow flavor by playing music composed by Tchaikovsky while it was fermenting." Out of curiosity, people line up to buy this product. Also recently, music therapy technology is being introduced in medical institutions, which is said to be the most scientific field. Additionally, theories saying that plants also have some kind of consciousness are becoming more and more published. When we grow plants and tell them sweet things such as "Please grow up healthy" or alternately by saying mean things such as, "Go on and get withered", these theories say that the plants show a clear difference in their growing progressions.

These theories made us think.

The water contained in food and plants must be listening to music and words.

People can become joyous and encouraged when they listen to music, all because the water contained in their bodies goes through a change.

The vibrations of music and words transmitted through the air affects water more than any other element.

"The vibrations of music and words affect the water that is contained in plants and food." Furthermore, "good music and kind words must exert a positive effect on water." Is there any way to demonstrate this theory? Pictures of crystals are wonderfully effective as a method to view the effect that music and words have on water.

Playing Music to Water

Playing Music to Water

How Do We Play Music to Water?

We selected distilled water as the water to experiment with because it has a simple crystal structure with the least number of impurities. We did find that some distilled water tends to lose the ability to form well-structured crystals. What you see here are only those samples that started out with well-formed crystals. First, we took pictures of basic distilled water; then after playing music (under the conditions shown in the upper right picture) we crystallized them and took their picture again.

"What is the best way to play music so that we get the optimum effects on the crystals? What should the genre of the music be? For how long? What is the volume? What should the distance from the speaker to the crystals be?" We had to spend a lot of time planning detailed experimentation methods. As a result of trial and error, we decided on the following procedure:

Place the distilled water in between 2 speakers and play one piece of music at a normal volume. Tap the bottom of the distilled water bottle and leave overnight. Tap well again the next day before freezing the water to make crystals. Take pictures of the crystals.

We do not know if this is the best method or not, but we feel that it is the best method that we know at this present point in time. In particular, tapping the container well is a rather important component because when we neglected to do it the crystallization rate declined. By applying this tapping vibration, information seemed to be transmitted through the water causing the crystals to activate. Anyway, these are the pictures of the crystals that were seen as a result of such strenuous efforts. Because there is no crystal that is identical to another, we obtained different crystal forms each time we took a picture. The next page confirms the similarities that can be found in pictures taken of 100 random samples. Following our music experiments, we decided to see how water responds to words. We also challenged ourselves to conduct experiments to see how much water is effected by human consciousness.

Similarity of Crystal Pictures

Pictures of the 100 samples are similar...

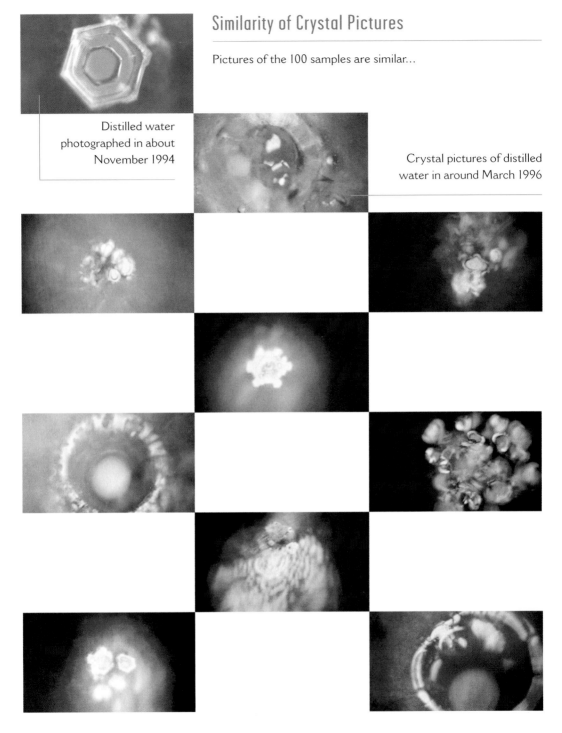

Distilled water photographed in about November 1994

Crystal pictures of distilled water in around March 1996

A sample of water that we placed as shown in bottom left picture on page 77 and then exposed to music showed some wonderful shapes.

The left hand pictures are pictures of the crystals from 100 basic distilled water, selected random.

Crystal pictures of distilled water after playing Hado music around March 1996

In the left hand pictures are crystals of water that have been exposed with a playing of a healing music called "Hado". This music is known for its ability to relax the body. In each container the shape of the crystals differed, but as you can see, we think that there are also some similarities.

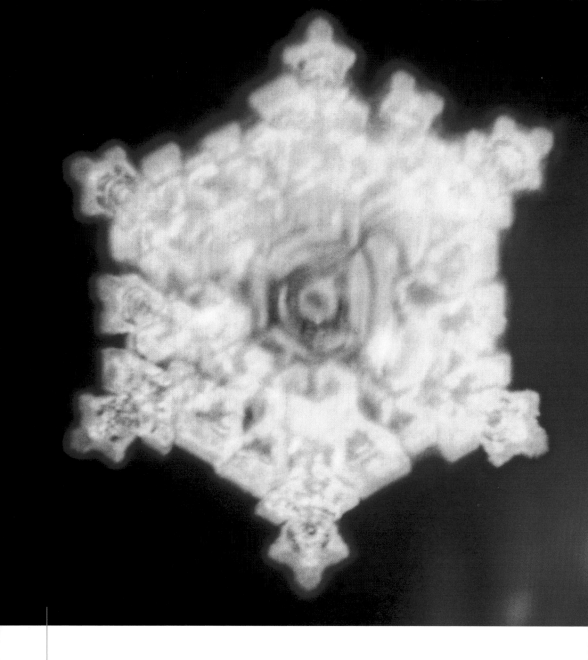

Beethoven's "Pastorale"

This is one of Beethoven's most famous symphonies and it is a bright, fresh and joyous piece.

This beautiful crystal supports the fact that good music positively affects water.

This symphony is a soulful song that seems to pursue beauty the most of any of the works of Mozart. A piece of deep thought that seems almost like a prayer to beauty. This music quietly heals the heart of its listeners. This crystal is so beautiful and graceful that it's as if it's speaking of the composer's feelings.

Bach's "Air on a G String"

Through this famous violin piece, the crystal seems as if it has been enchanted by the sound of the music. The branches of the water crystal stretch out freely.

This picture gives the impression that the crystal is dancing merrily.

"Bach's Goldberg Variations, which explores a vast emotional palette, is one of the greatest monuments of the keyboard repertoire."
As compared with crystals that grow from pure distilled water, here you can see that one hexagon is growing from the edge of another.

It is worth thinking about the feelings of thankfulness that are written into this set of variations and their ability to promote positive spiritual growth.

Chopin's "Farewell Song"

This is such a famous piano music piece that almost anyone can recognize this music once they hear it.

I have never been so astonished as I was when I obtained this crystal. Is it shaped the way that it is because it is affected by "Farewell Song"?

The basic crystal shape is almost perfectly divided into small parts that have become "separated" from each other. Despite the magnifying power of the microscope it is the same as it was in the other photos.

This is a picture of a crystal of water that has been exposed to a CD of healing music (composed by Alan Roubik) that was created in the USA. This music is said to make use of a special technology with the purpose of easing pain and enhancing physical immunity. The branch section of the crystal stretches out and becomes elongated. The resulting picture is beautiful, resembling a highly nutritious mushroom. We have received many reports from users that also felt various physiological effects by listening to this piece.

Tibet Sutra

This is a picture of crystal of water that formed after being exposed to a CD of the music from the soundtrack of the movie "Seven Years in Tibet."

We were able to take a picture of a powerful and beautiful crystal. We can reaffirm the ancient knowledge that the Sutra talks to people's souls and has a strong positive energy that can heal people's feelings.

This is a famous Korean folk song about two lovers who are forced to be separated as they cross the Arian mountain pass.

The girl sends off her departing lover with a song sung by Sugawara Tsuzuko.
Doesn't this crystal look somewhat painful, sad and heartbreaking?

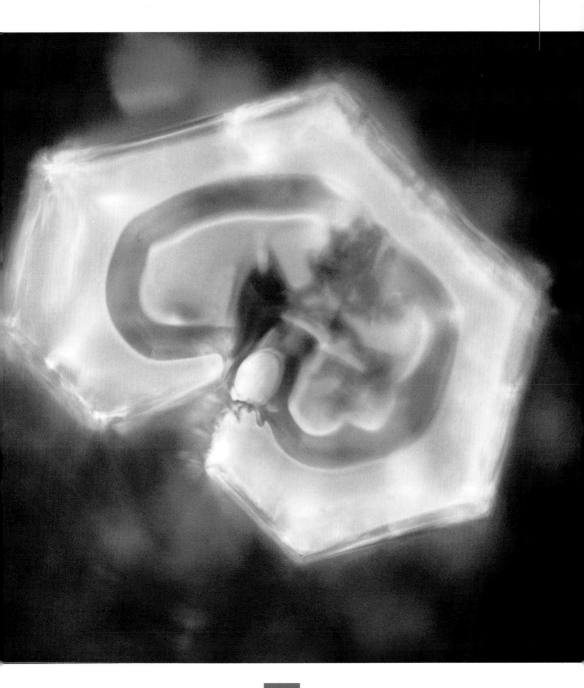

Kawachi Folk Dance Song

A folk dance song that has been handed down in the Kawachi region for more than 800 years. This is a crystal of water that we exposed to Kawachi Folk Dance Song. This idea was suggested by Mr. Kawachiya Kikusuimaru and was sung by himself.

For hundreds of years this music has been cherished and sung by many people, and because of this it may have some healing power.

How about trying popular music as compared with classical music and healing music? "Just Like a Flowing River" was sung by Misora Hibari, a famous singer of the Showa era. When this timeless and wonderful piece was sung,

there can be no doubts as to its positive energy and HADO. The crystal that formed is well-balanced in a way that reflects the nostalgic feelings of the listeners.

But what is the meaning of the gaping hole?

Folk Song of Celtic Region, UK

This music is sung by Enya who is well-known in Japan and elsewhere. We used the piece "Gaia Symphony No. 1," which is said to have the healing effects of relaxation. Each piece of her music has its own mystical unique world. This picture shows a tender and delicately beautiful crystal.

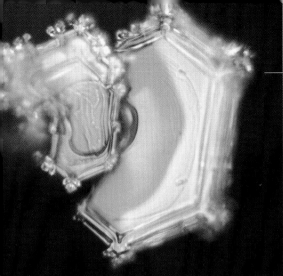

When we exposed the water to "Heartbreak Hotel" sung by Elvis Presley, we were able to obtain three types of crystals.

The picture in the upper left corner is a picture of a heart broken into two.

The picture above shows the two parts trying to fuse together.

The picture on the left shows a newly formed heart that overcame the difficult period.

Do you think that this idea is too sentimental?

Heavy Metal Music

This music is filled with anger and seems to be denouncing the world. Subsequently, this crystal's basic well-formed hexagonal structure has broken into perfect pieces. The water seems to have reacted negatively to this music. We are not saying that heavy metal music is bad, only that there must have been a problem with the lyrics. This is merely an example.

This is a song that is sung by a group that is very popular in Japan, and it is always at the top of the hit chart. However, when we look at the crystal, we can see its broken hexagonal structure and its subsequently square unattractive shape.

We are introducing this example only to show that popular music does not always contribute to the production of well-formed crystals.

Saying "Thank you" and "You fool" to Rice Everyday

When delivering a presentation on the experiment that we did with the effects of language on water (see page 95), one of the audience members told me that they were very impressed. This person also told me about an interesting experiment. This experiment involved placing cooked rice in two identical glass containers. Then he/she talked to the rice everyday saying "Thank you" to one and "You fool" to the other. He/she did this for one month to see the results. Two elementary school children talked to the rice everyday for one month as soon as they came home from school. As a result, the rice that the children had said "Thank you" to, was nearly fermented and had a nice mellow malted rice aroma. The other bowl of rice that the children had said "You fool" to, had turned black and had rotted. They said that its smell was disgusting beyond description.

Of course this is not an experiment that an official research institute did, so the result could have been just a coincidence. However, many people have done the same experiment and they showed the same results. Here, not only water but microbes seem to be involved. Microbes are just like us, they work hard if they are praised and become idle if they are abused. It seems that by saying "Thank you" and "You fool", the microbes have grouped into beneficial bacteria and disadvantageous bacteria.

Showing Letters
to Water

Does Water Change after Showing Words to It?

The water crystals showed various reactions to being exposed to music. So much so that we could not even have imagined the effects. Our next question led us to ask, what kind of reaction does water show towards words or the sounds that words make? For instance, there is a great difference between angrily yelling "You fool!" and saying "You are a fool" in a gentle way.

So we decided to use language with our water samples. In other words, to "speak" to our water. We decided not to use handwritten words but rather words that were typed by a word processor. Looking back, our idea of speaking to water may have deviated from general common sense, but the photography team simply went on with the idea.

For the base water on which to experiment, we used basic distilled water. This was the same water that we used for experimenting with music.

We divided this water sample into two parts and placed them into glass bottles. We then pasted a paper on one bottle that had "Thank you" typed on it. On the other bottle we put "You fool". We then left them both that way for one night. The next day we froze this water and took pictures of the crystals that formed. What we found was that the two water samples showed striking differences. We did the experiments without giving any information to the experimenting team. We also changed the experiment staff and ran the tests again, but we obtained the same results both times.

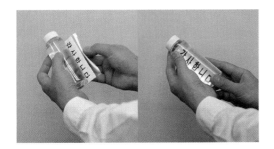

Thank you
in Japanese

ありがとう

Thank You

In this experiment we used basic distilled water and the words "Thank you" in the same way as we did in the "You fool" experiment. The crystal has a very beautiful, well-balanced shape.

It has a similar shape as the crystal that was exposed to "Goldberg Variations" on page 83. "Goldberg Variations" was composed by Bach to express his gratitude. The word "Thank you" in Japanese exists to help us express gratitude. Korean and English must have been derived differently.

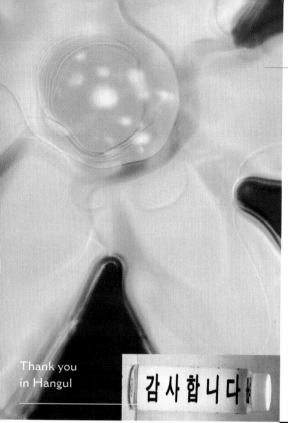

Thank you
in Hangul

감사합니다

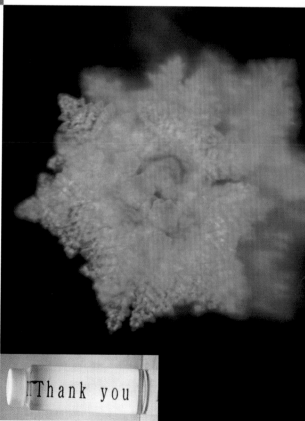

Thank you

You Fool

This is the water that had the word "You fool" on its bottle overnight. This crystal is similar to the one from the water that was exposed to heavy metal music on page 92. The lyrics of the music were similar to saying "You fool" to society, so the effect may have been the same. We also pasted the words "You fool" in English to another bottle. It seems that there is difference in the etymology of words because we did not obtain the same results.

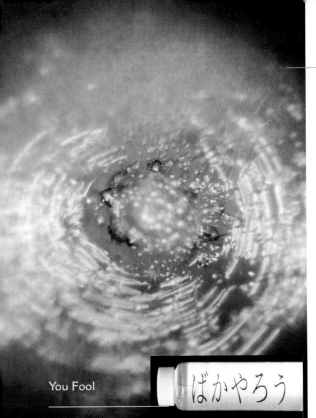

You Fool ばかやろう

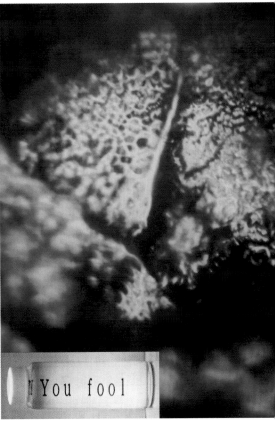

You fool

These are words that young people often use these days. Subsequently, the shape of the water was as ugly as we had expected after we exposed the sample to these words. The crystal was distorted, imploded and dispersed.

It really was a visual image of the words "you make me sick" and "I will kill you." That we exist in a world where words like this are used is awe-inspiring. We have to do something ourselves.

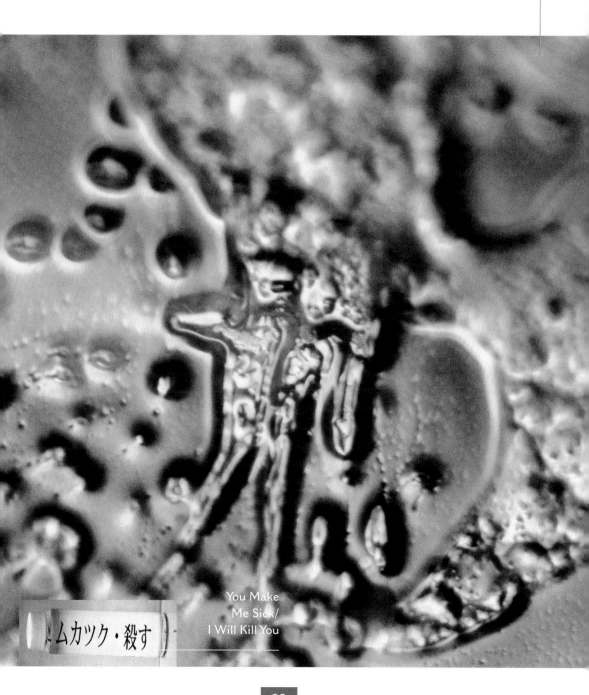

ムカツク・殺す

You Make
Me Sick/
I Will Kill You

Love/
Appreciation

愛 感謝

Love/Appreciation

People's consciousness contains love and appreciation. We took pictures of numerous crystals from this sample but this was the very first beautiful crystal that we saw.
Indeed, there is nothing more important than love and gratitude in this world. Just by expressing love and gratitude, the water around us and in our bodies changes so beautifully. We want to apply this in our daily lives, don't we? The strong resemblance to the crystal with the words "Thank you" on page 97 was a happy coincidence.

魂 Soul

Soul/Demon

When we remove the left part of the character for "soul" (which means "telling") we get the character for "demon". People become demons if they do not express their opinions. In this picture, the water crystal recognizes the word soul and give us humans this message. What kind of impression do the two pictures give us? Is it exaggerating to see a heart shape in the center?

Soul

魂

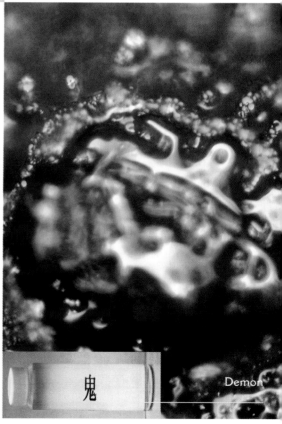

鬼

Demon

天使　　　Angel

Angel   天使

What do you think?

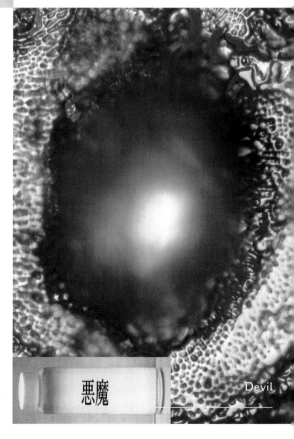

悪魔   Devil

しようね　　Let's Do It

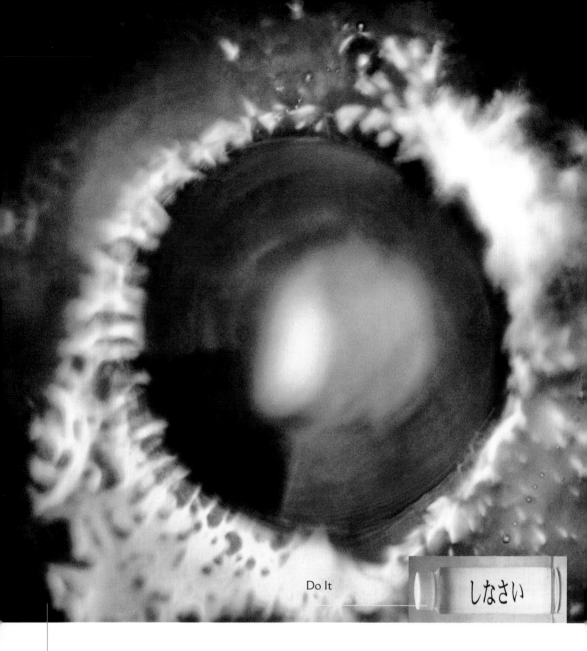

Do It しなさい

Let's Do It/Do It

We wanted to see if a word that was commanding (such as "Do it") and a word that was encouraging (such as "Let's do it") showed different results. These are words that we use everyday without thinking about it, but we should not abuse these words by using them too easily.

It is surprising to see what the effect of a negative word to the crystals is.

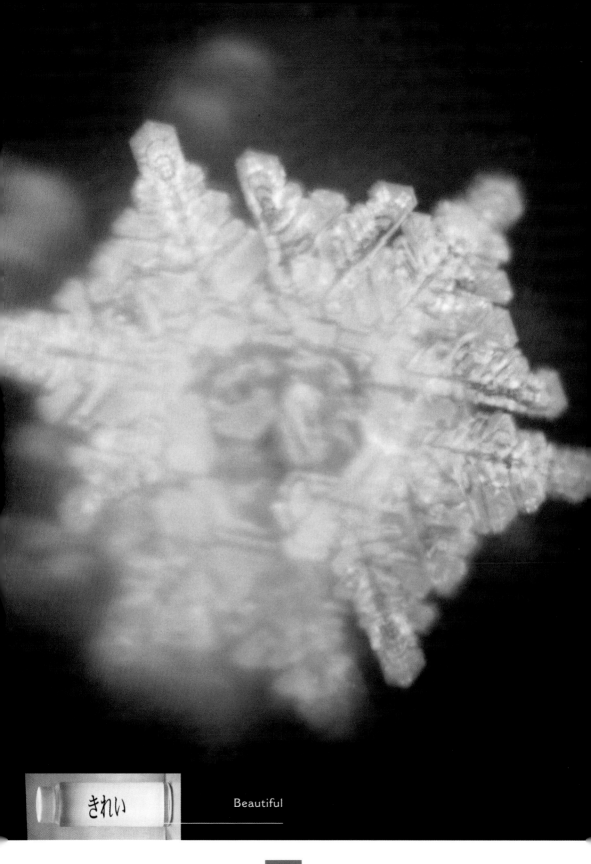

きれい　　　　　　　Beautiful

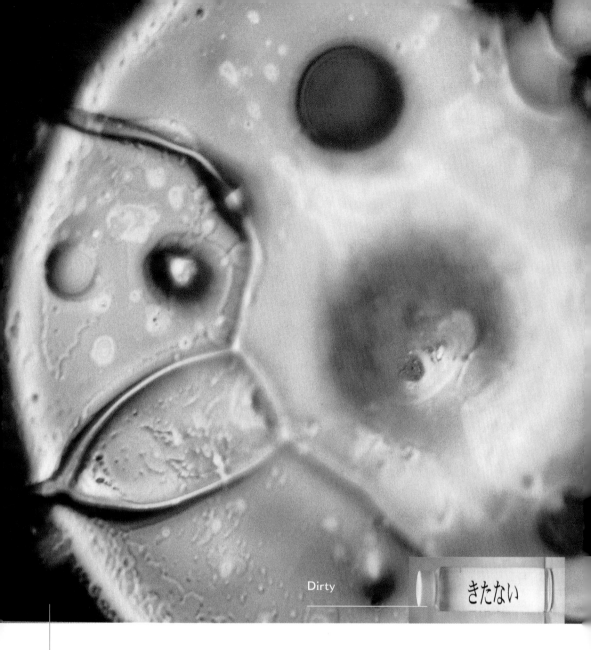

Dirty | きたない

Beautiful/Dirty

The water that we exposed to the letters of "beautiful" developed a beautiful crystal and the water that we exposed to the word "Ugly" had ugly crystals. These pictures show, in more ways than we had imagined, that letters and words have a big influence on water crystals.

Showing a Person's
Name to Water

With Feeling of Gratitude

The photography staff was astonished when hearing of this idea. The reason why I decided to expose water to people's names is due to the following sequence of events.

When Mr. M, who was an executive of a company, learned about the properties of HADO 2 of his children and 3 employees became

instructors in teaching the properties of HADO. Then their relationship, which was not too well, improved. Because of this experience he was eager to cooperate in my research.

I had been wondering for some time how I should thank him for his kindness. So, as a gift, I decided to paste a label on some samples of water that said "Mr. M's love" and to take a picture of the crystal that developed. Then, more than I had expected, all 100 water samples developed into beautiful crystal pictures.

I was so impressed that I put them in a frame and gave it to him as a present. Needless to say, it made him very happy. After that, I used the names of deceased people, the names of people who invited me to give lectures and names people who were on my mind.

I myself am not devoted to any religion and for some names of people mentioned it cannot be said whether they actually existed or whether they were just a myth.

Deguchi
Onisaburo

出口王仁三郎

Deguchi Onisaburo

Born in Kyoto, he married Deguchi Nao's daughter and created a religious association to try to raise the study of modern forms of religion.

Amaterasu Omikami is the most important Japanese God. A beautiful crystal developed as we imagined that it would.

Each branch of the crystal looks like the pendant paper strips that a Shinto shrine uses in its divine services. The center of crystal looks like the Divine Mirror, as the Shinto religion calls God's spirit. I can feel light slightly shining from the center. The shape like the sun appeared in the center of the crystal taken after 10 seconds from the first one. The crystal was developing and it had a shape that looked like the Divine Mirror.

天照大神

Amaterasu
Omikami

Developing crystal 10 seconds after
photographing

This is an experiment in which we exposed water to pictures instead of to words. We placed a picture of a toddler's smiling face on a sample of our basic distilled water. The branch part of the crystal stretches out energetically. People have commented that it gives them the impression of relaxation.

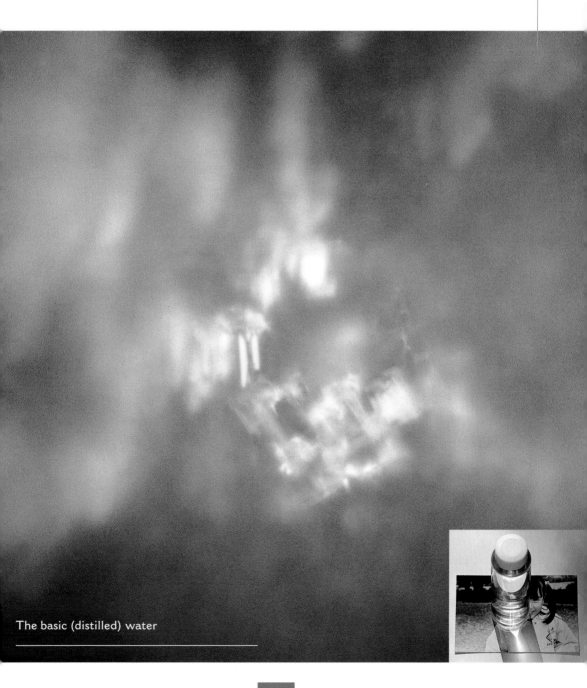

The basic (distilled) water

Water crystal after exposing the picture of
the innocent child to the basic (distilled)
water.

Water that had been shown a photograph of cherry blossoms demonstrated an ice crystal similar to the cherry blossom.

Still it was not a pentagon. (There are five petals in a cherry blossom.)

Photograph of cherry blossoms

Photograph of Stonehenge

We showed water a photograph of Stonehenge, that is located in the southern part of the United Kingdom. Some people say the stones are displaying the direction.

Surely, we could observe an ice crystal that is showing the direction of the north and the south as if it were the needle of a compass.

The Heidate Jinguu Shrine is quietly situated in the southern part of Aso in the Kyusyu Island of Japan. The resultant crystal also showed as if the Hei was raised. (Heidate means to raise a Hei, and Hei means a kind of flag to dedicate to the Deity in Shintoism.)

Photograph of a Heidate Jinguu Shrine

Painting

A painting "Dainichi Nyorai" by Ryu Keiko, who is said to be a painter of universal energy, was shown to water. The crystal showed a shape similar to the crystal that was obtained when a label "Universe" was shown to water. I understand this, since Dainichi Nyorai is said to be the God of the Universe. (Dainichi Nyorai is the God of the Universe in esoteric Buddhism.)

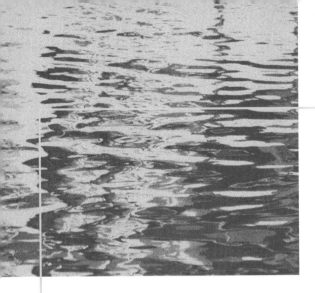

CHAPTER 3

M. Emoto/ The World of Water Spreads Afar

What is HADO/Chi?

All substances are composed of combinations of atoms. Atoms are composed of electrons and an atomic nucleus. Because electrons are negative and the atomic nucleus is positive, electrons orbit around the atomic nucleus at an ultra high speed and emit unique, faint vibration waves. This is what we call HADO.

The HADO moves around at an intense speed by electrons electrically pulling at each other and pushing away from each other. This motion forms a pattern (Magnetic Resonance Field), of which there are not two alike. This is what is called "Chaos" in modern science.

There is regularity in the atomic nucleus level, but the elementary particle that is found in atoms has no regularity in modern science. The reason is that it changes according to the consciousness of observers, by the way they see things. The world of the neutrino is at the same consciousness level as that of human beings.

That is why the root level of matter depends on people's consciousness.

Despite the fact that HADO is a very important phenomenon, it has been neglected in the development of general science, simply because it is invisible. I am an outsider. I am not in a professional position. So I am actually at an advantage and I could express the idea of trying to put HADO energy into "a visible form by using water crystals as material and canvas."

When we apply the principle the intensity of wave motion for instance, the health and stability of a creature's mind (good or bad) as well as the condition of the water can affect the process.

HADO is the minimum unit of invisible energy. Sound and electricity also have HADO.

Try to remember the tuning fork experiment that you did in your science class in junior high. You placed two tuning forks of the same frequency in line and then sounded one tuning fork. The sound was transmitted to the other tuning fork and resonated without making contact. This is called resonance.

This method of energy transmission through resonance is used in televisions, radios and cellular phones.

There are many things around us that actually make use of HADO technology.

A machine, "MRA (Magnetic Resonance Analyzer)," which measures various states of HADO, encodes the unique energy pattern of each substance and checks whether it resonates or not, was first developed in the USA 12 years ago.

This machine that makes the measurement of HADO possible is called the Magnetic Resonance Analyzer (MRA).

The saving/storing information and the wave motion technology that I had been doing research on had been united.

In the 11 years since I started my research on "HADO and Water," I have published 11 books, some of which have become bestsellers. (Please refer to page 9.)

"Transcript Technology" that Changes Water Artificially

Mr. Yukio Funai, mentioned on page 135, added the spirit of love to water in his own way for transcription. I didn't think any other layman could do such a thing.

HADO measuring instruments, including the MRA (currently, there are many types of HADO measuring instruments, including some domestic models), have HADO transcribing functions. The measurement first starts when the MRA puts out a faint resonance magnetic field, which is then transmitted to the subject and substances to be measured. Then the existence of resonance is checked. By amplifying the output of the measuring instrument HADO information can be transcribed.

The information is transcribed on to water because water has the highest retention capacity of information.

We also tried transcribing and photographing an immunity code (HADO information of normal immune strength) on to tap water and dam water with the MRA. After taking many crystal pictures we confirmed that crystals of water that have a high immune strength always have a firm tortoiseshell form.

It was made clear that when we transcribed the same information on to the same type of water, we obtained crystal pictures that had the same tendencies.

We were able to prove that a big change could be seen in pictures of water crystals that we had taken when no change was evident after the same crystals were studied through conventional scientific methods.

We hear that trees at the upper reaches of the Amazon River are being logged for their potential cure-all effects as drugs. This transcription technology is approved by people. However, if those same people were to understand the effects of transcribing this kind of information, I know that it would help them to effectuate environmental protection laws. I hope that day will come soon.

We took a picture of a change occurring in water by transcribing the HADO information of an immune code with the MRA on to a tap water sample from Shinagawa, Tokyo. The unaltered water on the left is the tap water of Tokyo. Its crystal formation is so grotesque. This second picture shows change to such an extent that it it is hard to believe that it is the same water that was used for the first crystal. It is natural to think that some kind of energy was applied to the water for such change to take place. This is what we call HADO. I would like to add that there is a similarity in the energy patterns emitted from a HADO measuring instrument, the MRA, as shown by the fact that the 2 crystals are of the same shape to a certain degree. For instance, we transcribed a immune HADO and did a survey using many types of water. As can be seen in culture 200 on page 122, we were able to obtain a wonderful tortoiseshell shaped crystal.

Tap water in Shinagawa before giving immune information.

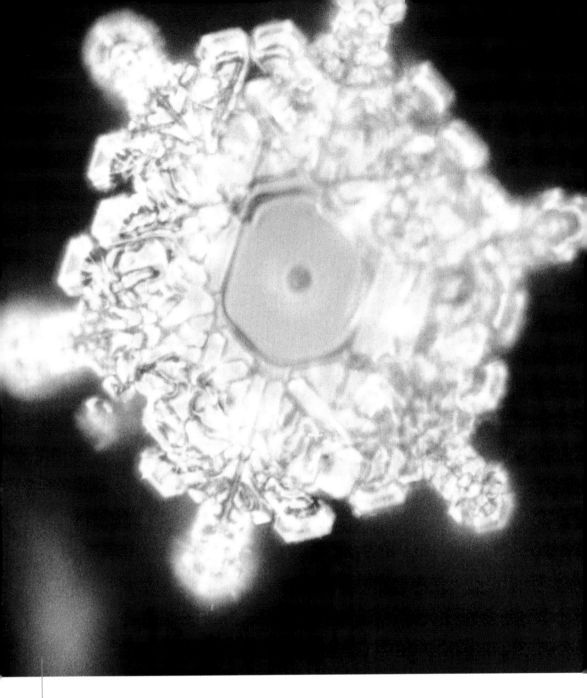

Tap water of Shinagawa after giving
immune information.

Transcription of HADO Information onto Futase Damo of Chichibu Lake, Saitama Prefecture

Most of the present dams are stagnant where many Aoko (blue green algae) live, and acidification at these dams is progressing. The dam stops water from flowing swiftly, thus keeping the water in an unnatural state.

This disrupts the ecosystem on the periphery of the dam. The water then flows down river in an acidified form, contaminating the vicinity and destroying nature.

While harboring earnest feelings for its improvement, we transcribed the necessary wave motion to the dam water. As a result we came out with a picture of a beautiful crystal. We are confident that if we make and develop a large transcribing device we can improve dam water.

By the way, when taking the photographs of the dam crystals we also came out with an unexpected picture.

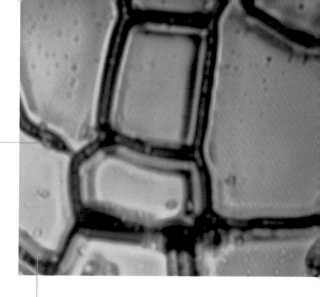

Source water in dam

The pictures on the next page were taken every 5 seconds and you can see that the first picture and the picture taken 5 seconds later have reversed red and green areas.

We do not know what this means but this will be a future topic of study for us.

After transcription

The first picture in the series of pictures

After 5 seconds

After 10 seconds

After 20 seconds

After 25 seconds

Camomile

Transcribing aroma oil to water.

Crystal picture of camomile water

HADO information that aromatherapy oil contains was transcribed to a water sample and was frozen before taking the crystal's picture. We were surprised to obtain a picture of a crystal that is similar to the look of the flowers that the different aroma oils were made from. These crystals may resemble the shape of the substance.

Fennel

Crystal picture of fennel water

Water Changed by People's Consciousness

Water Reflects People's Consciousness

Our attempt at exposing water to language had greater results than we had expected. So far, we had very interesting experiences with exposing water to music, to language and to names. With the results of this experiment, we were able to formulate a hypothesis that information can be transmitted through "Shapes", such as words and pictures.

We did not expect though, that the crystals would show such dramatic and clear changes. We have become aware that water stores and transmits information.

After obtaining results like this, we could not resist stepping into the territory of human consciousness? We wanted to find out what kind of change thought could cause.

The idea started after a sad and painful experience that we had four years ago. Immediately after the Great Hanshin-Awaji earthquake, the crystal pictures of the water from Kobe had something greatly inherent in human consciousness. To prove this, 3 months afterwards, the water in Kobe changed greatly. We would like to show the crystal picture changed by people's consciousness.

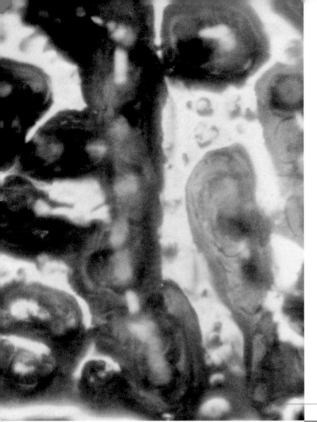

The Great Hanshin-Awaji Earthquake and Tap Water

On January 17, 1995, the Great Hanshin-Awaji earthquake took place in Kobe. Three days afterwards we took pictures of the crystals found in the tap water in Kobe (that was available at that time). It is as if the water captured the fear, panic and deep sorrow of the people immediately after the earthquake. The crystals were completely destroyed. It was a picture that made people shudder.

We felt that we could not make this public because of the horror of its extreme misery.

Immediately after the Great Hanshin-Awaji Earthquake

However, 3 months later... Helping hands and sympathy from all over the world reached out to the people of Kobe. Also since no riots occurred the people of Kobe were praised by many people.

Although the rubble piled up high, people were able to restore their environment due the kindness and warmth of others. This crystal seems to have collected these feelings also.

3 months after the Earthquake

I sent letters to 500 HADO instructors across Japan (graduates of my HADO study). "At 2:00 on February 2, 1997, I will leave a cup containing the tap water of Shinagawa-ku on the table in my office. Please transmit your feelings to that water at the same time from all over Japan. Of course, for this water to become a clean water, please send 'Chi and Soul' of love and the wish that the water should become clean. Thank you very much."

In this way, water received "Chi and Soul" from all over Japan. And this is the picture of crystal we obtained. (Please refer to page 134.)

Of course, no physical change had been made. We had not expected it but were able to obtain a clear change in the condition of the water. All of the staff were so impressed that they were almost ready to cry. We feel deeply appreciative of all those who cooperated with us from all over Japan. We started to feel that people's thoughts could be gathered regardless of how far apart they are.

Original water.
The picture of tap water in Shinagawa, Tokyo;
taken the day before

Water with "Chi, Soul and Spirit" of
500 People

This is a picture of a crystal of a tap water sample from Shinagawa-ku, Tokyo, to which Mr. Yukio Funai of Funai Consulting Co., Ltd., (a supporter of our research) applied "Chi of Love". I felt without a doubt that we could obtain well-formed crystals. However, because it was originally only ordinary tap water, we did not really expect that we could obtain such a beautiful crystal. This is called "Water is the mirror of mind." If this is possible, then it could also be possible to change controversial tap water to a beautiful crystal through the conscious thought of human beings. And this fact seems to indicate that our actions and words make water more beautiful and cleaner.

Water
and Soul

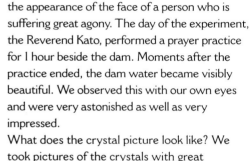

People's Consciousness and Crystals

Finally, this is a picture of a crystal of water obtained as a result of a water purification experiment "through soul" by the Reverend Kato Hoki, the chief priest of Jyuhouin temple, Omiya City. The experiment was conducted at the Fujiwara Dam in Minakami-cho, Gunma Prefecture.

In Japan, it is widely believed that the soul dwells in the spirit that is present in words. The picture of the crystal of water before the experiment is indeed horrifying and in fact has

the appearance of the face of a person who is suffering great agony. The day of the experiment, the Reverend Kato, performed a prayer practice for 1 hour beside the dam. Moments after the practice ended, the dam water became visibly beautiful. We observed this with our own eyes and were very astonished as well as very impressed.

What does the crystal picture look like? We took pictures of the crystals with great expectations and we obtained crystal pictures as beautiful as the one the cover.

We have never seen a more beautiful picture that emits brilliant energy as much as this one does. Amidst the basic hexagonal structure, there is also a small hexagon. This hexagon is an object d'art of light that is surrounded by an aura. The crescent portion at the center also seems to have a halo around it. People say that this picture makes them feel an immeasurable amount of power and energy in their soul based on people's consciousness. When energy based on people's love and appreciation harmonizes with water, why should such a wonderful thing seem so unreasonable?

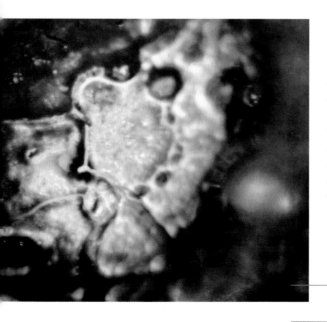

Water crystal of Fujiwara Dam
before offering an prayer

Waving water in dam before praying.

Still water in dam after praying.

Water of the lake became calm after praying.

After offering a prayer.

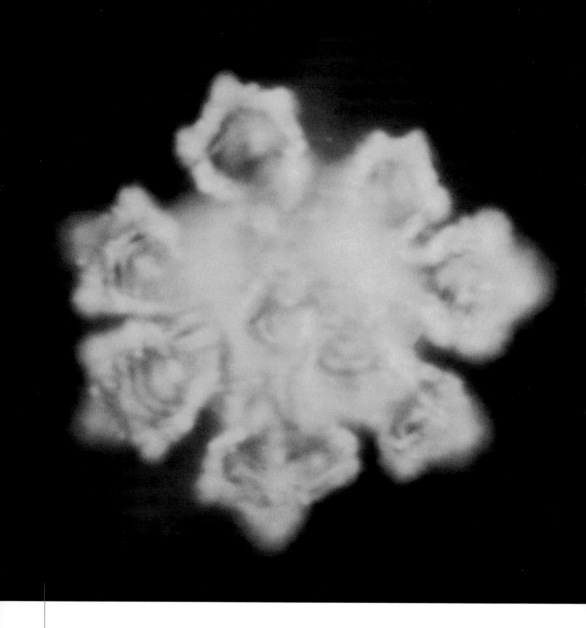

We Could Take a Heptagonal Crystal Picture

We were taking pictures of the dripping water of Fujiwara Dam while the Reverend Kato was giving prayers. During this shoot we obtained pictures of crystals as wonderful as those on the cover of this book.

Among them, we were able to obtain a few mysterious pictures of which this is one. In terms of beauty, there is nothing that compares to the one on the cover. Take a close look and you will be astonished to find that it is not a hexagon but a heptagon. We had never been able to obtain a picture of a heptagonal crystal before this experience. The Reverend Kato said he prayed to the Seven Benzaiten (Goddesses of Fortune).

Water has a variety of messages, but it seems that we have a lot to learn from messages we receive.

Water Came from the Space?

The Wonders of Water Become Even Deeper

Evaluating water by taking pictures of water crystals is a new approach that comes from a completely different viewpoint than that of the usual conventional scientific analysis and evaluation methods.

What we learned from these experiments is that we do not know anything about water. More questions and issues come up, one after another.

Let's start with the questions about the water that exists on earth.

Why does water exist? The origin of water used to be surrounded by mystery.

As the space probe advances, it has already been confirmed that water exists on Mars. We are starting to understand that water is not unique to earth but exists throughout space.

Article from the Asahi Shimbun,
Monday, June 2, 1997

"Water Came Flying from the Ultimate Limits of Space", from a Press Report in 1997

A Press Report in 997 the National Aeronautics and Space Administration (NASA) announced in May, 1997, that "We observed for the first time a snowball-shaped microscopic heavenly body flying in numerous numbers toward the stratosphere of earth from space." (Refer to the picture of the article on the bottom right of page 141.)

This announcement was reported in the NHK news and in national newspapers.

"This snowball is deemed to be a heavenly body similar to a small comet with a diameter of about a dozen meters. About few thousands of them come flying daily but as they come near the earth surface, they decompose and become a part of cloud".

In other words: rain comes falling from space everyday. This yearly quantity of "rain from space" may only be a small quantity, but if this has been going on got 4,6 billion years (since the origin of earth) it is large enough to be the source of the oceans.

Furthermore, this "rain from space" contains an organic substance and this indeed must be the origin of life. Similar research has been announced by an astronomical observatory at the University of Hawaii on August of the same year. (Please refer to the picture on the left.)

If this is true, the question of the unique and mysterious nature of water can be understood. If the origin of water is space, it is no wonder that its questions cannot be solved by the scientific powers that we have on earth. Space is too big for humans and it is an unimaginable entity. The truth of the matter is that, by researching water further, we may be able to understand more about space. The mere thought is very exciting.

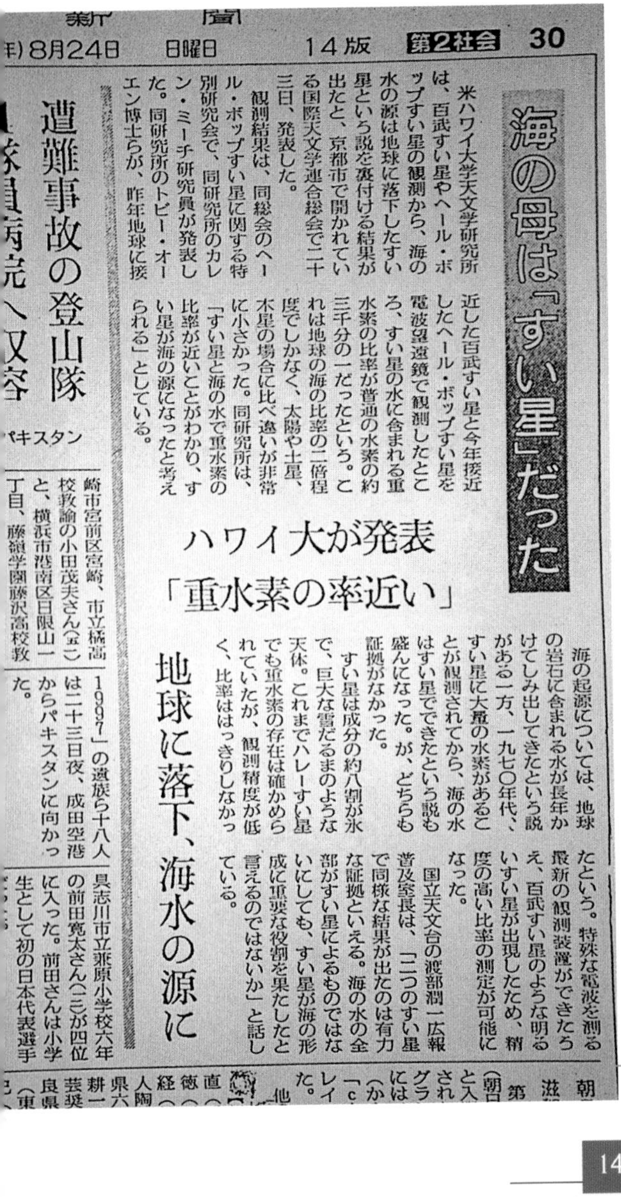

毎日新聞 ８月24日 日曜日 14版 第2社会 30

海の母は「すい星」だった

ハワイ大が発表 「重水素の率近い」

地球に落下、海水の源に

米ハワイ大学天文学研究所は、近づいた百武すい星と今年接近したヘール・ボップすい星の水の源は地球に落下したすい星という説を裏付ける結果が出たと、京都市で開かれた国際天文学連合総会で二十三日、発表した。

観測結果は、同総会のヘール・ボップすい星に関する特別研究会で、同研究所のカレン・ミーチ研究員が発表した。同研究所のトビー・オーエン博士らが、昨年地球に接近した百武すい星と今年接近したヘール・ボップすい星を電波望遠鏡で観測したところ、すい星の水に含まれる重水素の比率が普通の水素の約三千分の一だったという。これは地球の海の比率の二倍程度でしかなく、太陽や土星、木星の場合に比べ違いが非常に小さかった。同研究所の、「すい星と海の水でい星が近いことがわかり、すい星が海の源になったと考えられる」としている。

海の起源については、地球の岩石に含まれる水が長年かけてしみ出してきたという説、百武すい星のような明るいすい星が出現したため、精度の高い比率の測定が可能になった。すい星でできたという説とがあり、すい星の水素の比率が海の水の全体がすい星によるのではないにしても、すい星が海の形成に重要な役割を果たしたと言えるのではないか」と話している。

左側：遭難事故の登山隊 ／ パキスタン

Article of the Mainichi Shimbun, Sunday, August 24, 1997

142

Postscript

What was the impression you got from the pictures of crystals?

I am sure that you were astonished to find out that water shows such a variety of crystals due to its environment. Some of you may have asked the question, "Is it true?" And some of you may have believed this without a doubt.

I published this picture book with an earnest intention to propose new ideas. Things that are attempted for the first time always elicit criticism, and I am well-aware of that fact.

I think my work started from love for people and for the Earth.

All I ask for is for you to understand the great and secret aspects of water.

If water originally did not exist on earth and came from far away in space, it means that our existence also started in outer space.

No one could have any objections to our attempts to study water. In these experiments we have clung to water in an attempt to get more familiar with it, to harmonize with it and understand it. These are all very important things for humans to do.

Therefore, before I started my work I already mastered one technique. By practicing health consultation in the past, with a total of more than 10.000 people, I experienced the maintenance of health through water. For this reason, I developed a unique approach toward water. I had many deeply impressive feelings while systematizing and organizing this book. What is the destination of this chaotic world? What is the origin and history of humans? And how will it be in future? These are issues that everyone must think about very seriously. I feel that this picture book will serve as a concise text and valuable teaching tool to help people to take a closer look at water.

I hope that this book creates an opportunity for discussions about water to be raised all over the world and that other countries will join me in trying to do the same. To achieve this purpose, this book has been translated in English.

We will continue publishing: a 2nd edition and 3rd edition. I hope to receive opinions and responses from my readers which will enable me to lift this research to a higher scientific and philosophical level, and to not let it end in mere self-satisfaction.

Finally, I would like to express my deepest appreciation to Dr. Lee H. Lorenzen who helped to find my way in my research.

To Mr. Kazunari Ishibashi, Mr. Seiya Sato, Mr. Jun Futamura, and all the old and new staff members of IHM who engaged in this research. To Mr. Tokujiro Kawasaki, a landscape photographer, who takes beautiful pictures of Mother Nature.

To Mr. Shinya Taguchi, the former president of Nichirei Co. Ltd., whose life's work is the positive adjustment of overseas water. Thank you for sending me ice from all over the world. And to the members of the International HADO Friendship and their HADO instructors, who always supported us in my research. To the staffs of Sun Create, headed by Ms. Tsuneko Narukage, who organized the crystal pictures so wonderfully.

Masaru Emoto

Editor's Notes

This book contains pictures of crystals taken from September 1994 to April 1999.

After I had accepted the editing work, I took a first look at the refrigerating room used for photographing the crystals. I saw a solid refrigerating room (about the size of a tatami mat), a desk, a freezer, and a camera with a microscope attached on top. The refrigerator was filled with Petri dishes. What was most impressive was the heavy down jackets and pants that were hung in front of the refrigerating room. The season had already turned to spring and it was right after the full blooming of cherry blossoms. The crystal photography staff kept saying "It's cold, it's cold" throughout the year. It was like spending winter in the Antarctic.

A numerous amount of crystal pictures was stored as data and is waiting for its turn to serve the world and mankind.

Who in the world, except for Emoto Masaru, would think of pasting papers typed with "Thank you" or "Amaterasu Omikami" on a bottle containing water. We all kept saying that. But now we, the staff, are encouraging him to plan a second edition of this book.

He said it just came across his mind. Since his research was based on the deep feelings towards water that he had accumulated over the years, he was very serious. Now it is gradually bearing fruit.

Up until now, the experiment that we carried out tormented us with feelings that we would never be understood by anyone. It was hard for us. But I suppose the staff who were actually engaged in the photography were having the most fun. They screamed out astonishment and enthusiasm everyday as we stepped in to a world that no one else has ever explored.

I admire Emoto Masaru for organizing and storing a tremendous amount of data with the support and cooperation of many people.

I would like to express my gratitude to him for giving me this chance to do interesting work.

Tsuneko Narukage

Referred books and music

Book
'The day that lightning chased the housewife'
Julia Leigh and David Savoid, Shobun-sha
Publisher

CD
Beethoven 'Pastorale'
'Super Best 101'
Beethoven's symphony No. 6, 'Pastorale'
Berliner Philharmonishe Orchester

Mozart's 'Symphony No. 40 in G Minor'
'Very Best Classics' Symphony No. 40 in
G Minor K550
Britain/UK Chamber Orchestra

Bach's 'Air on a G String'
'Once upon a time classics-love'
Air on a G String Orchestral/Suite No. 3 in
D Major BWV 1068

Bach's 'Goldberg Variations'
'Goldberg Variations/4 Duets'
Goldberg Variations BWV998

Chopin's 'Farewell Song'
Chopin/Famous Pieces for Piano-Farewell
Song Etude in E. Major, Op. 10, No. 3

Healing music (HADO)
HADO Music 'A blending of science and music'
immune system Pain Relief Series 1

Tibet Sutra
'World Music'
Chanting holy invocation of esoteric Buddhism
'Sound track'

Korean Folk Song 'Ariran'
Sugawara Tsuzuko Collection

'Kawachi Chorus song'
'Kawachi Chorus Song/Kawachi Kikusuimaru'
Bob Marley Story '97

Just Like A Flowing River
'Misora hibari/Original Best Hit 50'

Folk Song of Celtic Region, England
'Enya Paint the Sky - The Best of Enya'

'Heartbreak Hotel'
'Mega Elvis the essential collection'

Thank you very much.

Masaru Emoto

Born in Yokohama in July 1943.
Graduated from International Relationships
Course, Department of Humanities and
Sciences, Yokohama City University.
Established I.H.M. Co., Ltd. in 1986 after
working for Chisan Co., Ltd. and Chubu
Yomiuri Shimbun (Central HQ of the Yomiuri
Shimbun at present).
Certified and licensed degree of docter of alter-
native medicine from Open International
University in October, 1992. Challenges myste-
riousness of water after encountering MRA,
Magnetic Resonance Analyzer and micro-clus-
ter water in the USA.
Aims at research of various kinds of water, such
as water in a human body, water in daily life,
and water on Earth from the point of personal
aspect rather than scientific one. Continues
creative experiments on the basis of belief that
water crystals reflect the essence of water.
At present, President of I.H.M. General
Research Institute, I.H.M. Co., Ltd., and
I.H.M. International HADO Membership.
Wrote a number of books such as "The Prelude
to the Hado Age" published by Sun Road
Publishing Co., Ltd.

Masaru Emoto
I.H.M. Co. LTD
Eastside Bldg. 1F, 1-1-11
Yanagibashi, Taito-ku, Tokyo 111-0052
Japan
Tel: 81-3-3863-0211
Fax: 81-3-3866-5353
ihm@hado.com

Messages from Water
ISBN 908074213-9
Edited by Masaru Emoto
Photographed by Kazuki Hamano, Kazunari
Ishibashi, Masaya Sato / I.H.M. General
Research Institute
Printed in the Republic of Czech

Published by
Hado Publishing BV
Sluisvaart 66
1191 HE Ouderkerk a/d Amstel
The Netherlands
Tel: 31-20-472-1838
Fax: 31-20-472-1839
book@hado.net
www.hado.net

Copyright © 1999 Hado Kyoikusha Co. Ltd
Hado Kyoikusha Co. Ltd
Eastside Bldg. 1F, 1-1-11
Yanagibashi, Taito-ku, Tokyo 111-0052
Japan
Tel: 81-3-3863-0211
Fax: 81-3-3866-5353
info@hado.com

Translated by TMS Communications Ltd.
Compiled by Sun Create K.K.
Photo provided by Tokujiro Kawasaki
Layout by Studio Imago, Amersfoort,
the Netherlands
Edited by Studio Imago, Amersfoort,
the Netherlands

To order this book, please contact following distributors:

UK

Int'l. Flower Essence Repertoire Ltd.
The Living Tree
Milland
nr. Liphook, Hants GU30 7JS
England
tel. 01 428 741 572
Fax: 01 428 741 679
e-mail : flower@atlas.co.uk

IFER
Achamore House
Isle of Gigha
Scotland PA41 7AD
Tel. 01 583 505 385
e-mail : flower@atlas.co.uk

North America

Source Books, Inc.
PO Box 292231
Nashville, TN 37229-2231
1-800-637-5222 or 1-615-773-7691
fax 1-615-773-7016
www.sacredspaces.org

Other countries

Hado Publishing BV
Sluisvaart 66
1191HE Ouderkerk a/d Amstel
The Netherlands
Tel : +31-20-472-1838
Fax : +31-20-472-1839
E-mail : book@hado.net